Making Natural Hoof Care Work for You

Making Natural Hoof Care Work for You

A Hands-On Manual for Natural Hoof Care
All Breeds of Horses and All Equestrian Disciplines
For Horse Owners, Farriers, and Veterinarians

PETE RAMEY

foreword by JAIME JACKSON

Star Ridge Publishing
Natural Horse Care Library

Design by Star Ridge Publishing.

Cover photo: Cindy Sullivan

Printed in the United States of America.

First printing, September 2003

ISBN 0-9658007-7-6

Star Ridge Publishing
P.O. Box 2181
Harrison, AR 72601
1-870-743-4603
1-870-743-1637 (FAX)
www.star-ridge.com

Neither the author, Star Ridge Publishing, nor any individual
or organization quoted in this book accept responsibility for
any applications or misapplications of the ideas or procedures
presented herein. The publisher presumes in all instances that
horse owners will solicit the services of qualified hoof care
providers. Natural hoof care is a sophisticated and highly
technical process that should only be practiced by qualified
natural hoof care practitioners trained in high performance
barefooted trimming methods, or by persons under their
supervision.

Contents

foreword

It wasn't without a certain amount of trepidation that, a few years ago, I encouraged Pete to write a book about his experiences as a natural hoof care practitioner in Georgia. Not everyone who practices our artful science with proficiency and the highest levels of expertise, can also write about it. I'm proud to say that Pete has risen and met the challenge on all accounts, and with candor and unmitigated enthusiasm. With the publishing of *Making Natural Hoof Care Work for You*, horse owners will benefit from the astute observations and advice of a true expert.

Natural hoof care, contrary to what many unfamiliar with our profession might think, encompasses a very broad spectrum of opinions concerning how to interpret and best apply our model—the wild horse hoof—to the domestic horse. But this is true of any serious discipline. The value of books like Pete's is that they not only open doors to horse owners seeking better hoof care, but compel other hoof care professionals to challenge their own thinking and methods. I can think of few better ways to improve the quality of our profession and services.

There is something else remarkable about Pete's book that I want to bring to the reader's attention at the outset. A central theme of his book is "what the horses have taught me". This isn't lip service. To the contrary, humbly this is how Pete has learned, and it is clear to us as we look over his shoulder to hear him reason aloud toward solutions, grapple with the many uncertainties inherent in this work, and rejoice in his revelations and triumphs. Equally evident is that he has not forgotten his inspiration for becoming a natural hoof care practitioner in the first place: the wild horse. The reader is reminded that without this model, there would be no natural hoof care. Or this book and the benefits horses will derive from it.

— Jaime Jackson

(Clockwise from left) Pete Ramey, Ruth Green, Steve Dick, Cindy Sullivan, and Jaime Jackson.

Acknowledgements

I would like to thank Nancy and Jaime Jackson, and Cindy Sullivan for their lifetime of dedication and sacrifice on behalf of all the horses and for their inspiration and hard work on this book.

I also thank God for the "touch", the ability, and the insight He has given me. I thank my mother for my heart, my dad for my soul, and my daughter Lauren, for always keeping me in touch with the truly important things in life.

And to my unbelievable support group of close friends and wonderful family—thank you for being there. I couldn't have done it without you.

Since I wrote this book in 2000, some wonderful changes have happened in my life. I have a beautiful new daughter, Alyson. "You have brought me tremendous joy I just can't put into words." I have a new son, Clint, who can bring out the goofy kid in me like no one else in the world. These gifts and many, many more were given to me by my lovely bride, Ivy. "Thank you, Ivy, for all that you do. You are the most incredible partner, manager, best friend, lover, role model and teacher I could ever imagine." Ivy found me hiding from the world, happily maintaining 700 horses. She is the one that built the website, started organizing the clinics, made me start writing again and basically booted me out into the much larger world of teaching others. It seems her intuition and wisdom is helping many more horses than my tired old back ever would have. "Ivy, I will spend the rest of my life trying to repay you for the happiness you have given me. Thank you."

Pete Ramey
Georgia/2005

Important updates to this book and clinic
information available at www.hoofrehab.com

Introduction
Getting On the Same Page

I was first introduced to natural hoof care in 1998. A friend loaned me a copy of the *Horse Owners Guide to Natural Hoof Care* by Jaime Jackson. I read it, hoping to pick up some new hoof knowledge that would improve my shoeing. That book made so much sense to me I didn't have to take Jaime's word for even one sentence. Somehow I knew I was reading the truth. I decided to give it a try with my personal horse and was very pleased with his performance. I never intended to be a "barefoot advocate." It is easier to be mainstream and "go with the flow", but as I experimented with natural hooves I was so amazed by the fantastic results I was getting, I stopped perceiving any need for horseshoes almost immediately and at this time, can't imagine a situation in which I would need to nail one on.

I was shoeing the horses for a public trail riding facility in the north Georgia mountains. The owner was intrigued by the concept of natural hoof care, so we decided to see how it would work on horses that typically wore shoes to the thickness of a nickel in four or five weeks. I trimmed the horses to Jaime's guidelines and, to our amazement, the horses were okay. This country is rough, but the excessive wear we were expecting never happened. They kept putting out enough hoof wall to do the job, and then some. About 18 of them were perfectly sound from day one, but the other ten were too tender footed to be ridden on the mountain because they lacked natural sole concavity and were too "flat footed". Hoof boots would have made transition for those guys easy, but I'm almost thankful I didn't

Pete (wearing white cap) with students at one of several natural hoof care clinics he held in Norway during 2003. Natural trimming has become an international sensation, spreading to all continents.

Making Natural Hoof Care Work for You

have them back then. It was those ten horses that started me on the path to learning most of what I will share with you in this book.

Reading the *Horse Owners Guide to Natural Hoof Care* is prerequisite to learning anything from this book. In it, Jackson details the science and the nature behind natural hoof care. He details lifestyle and nutritional needs of horses, and that is more important to hooves than the trim itself. As far as hoof trimming goes, that book was only the beginning of a journey for me. I kept searching for ways to help those ten tender horses. I studied the Internet, which is packed with "barefoot stuff." Some of it is good, and some of it is pure hogwash. I read more books and kept studying, picking the brains of fellow farriers and barefoot trimmers, and I kept trimming horses every day. Those original ten horses became sound, and we started buying foundered horses and rehabilitating them. These days, I am trimming around eighty horses a week. I've learned a lot, and I've only scratched the tip of the iceberg. I get calls every day from people all over the country looking for help. There is no detailed natural trimming guide I can refer them to. Other people besides me have figured it out of course, but only by trial and error like I did. What we need is a book that explains barefoot trimming in detail that begins where the *HOG* leaves off. This is my goal.

This book will give newcomers to natural hoof care a wealth of advantages I did not have. Still, there is no substitute for experience. Teaching hoof trimming is a nightmare because there is so much judgment involved. No formulas will work, because every hoof is different. We must learn to listen to what the hoof is trying to tell us. Learn all you can and by all means learn from your mistakes. If the horse is less comfortable after you trim, you messed up. Figure out why, and don't make that mistake next time.

In the beginning, I trimmed the horses at the riding stable on Monday, so they would have all week to "recover" from my trimming and be at their best for the busy weekend ahead. As time passed, I learned a little more and started trimming them on Friday because I now could make them go *better* right after a trim. More time passed and I learned a little more and now trim them whenever I please, usually on the weekend between rides because they are always totally sound. Even new horses that come in shod can be comfortably put right to work barefoot if their hooves are already fairly healthy. It is this learning period I struggled through that I hope to shorten or eliminate for readers of this book.

I am an "under the horse" person, not a scientist. This book is written in simple terms but is intended for people with a working knowledge of horses and their hooves. It is assumed that you have read and understand the prerequisite material so I won't waste your time by feeding it to you all over again. It has been incredibly difficult to put these trimming methods on paper because it is such a hands-on subject, and I highly recommend for any beginner to seek the personal guidance of a competent professional who has been successful in creating many sound barefoot riding horses.

I am against the use of nailed-on metal horseshoes. It is well-documented that they harm the hoof by causing contraction, bacterial invasion, and significant loss of shock absorption. Worse yet, the shoe stops natural hoof wear, allowing excessive length to cause all sorts of unnatural forces to pry away at the hoof structure and the limbs. Most of the protection the shoe offers is in peoples' heads, anyway. How does a ¼ inch thick band of metal around the outside perimeter of the hoof help a horse withstand riding on one inch diameter rocks? People don't start putting shoes on young horses because of foot pain, anyway. People put shoes on young horses out of fear and habit. The pain comes later after the shoe has weakened the hoof. The horse was very successfully ridden far more aggressively than we ride now for some 7000 years before the horseshoe was invented. Horseshoes are simply a bad idea and it is time for the world to move past them. *The damage caused by horseshoes is no secret and in my opinion doing damage to an animal to make it better suit our needs is inherently wrong.* That said, this book is not a farrier bashing. The most important part of any shoeing job is the trim, and this book is about trimming. The farrier industry has been searching for alternatives to the horseshoe for decades for the *same* reasons I don't like them.

I'll never understand how farriers and natural hoof care practitioners got divided into two camps at war, but I'm here to bridge that gap. We're all on the same team. We all want the very best for the horse. It is a fact that wild horse research has revealed some major findings about horses and their hooves, and it is also a fact that competent farriers are the most capable of bringing those findings to aid the horses if they will only take the time to check out what we have learned.

I first started studying natural hoof care to improve my own shoeing. I was reading every farrier and veterinary text I could get my hands on because there seemed to be so little information out there about the actual hoof. The "barefoot" books and websites were just another possible source of information on hooves, and to my surprise they helped me unravel most of the hoof problems that had been perplexing me. There's not a farrier on the planet that doesn't have a few unanswered questions rattling around in his or her head. We all have a lot to learn, for sure, and if one farrier picks up this book and finds one shred of information that helps one horse, I will consider the whole ordeal a success.

We in the "natural hoof care camp" have endured a huge controversy, fueled by misunderstanding and by the fact that some very vocal, public people are making major mistakes in hoof trimming and attempting to justify trimming guidelines that lead to sore horses. That is not what this book or natural hoof care is about. Pick up any farrier text and you will find that they all encourage long unshod periods for horses to heal the hooves from the effects of continuous shoeing. In natural hoof care, we simply take things a step further and allow this healing to continue throughout the horse's life. Meanwhile, we use professionally fitted hoof boots for protection when the terrain demands are too tough for the conditioning or current health of the hooves. It's that simple. As this healing continues, the result over time is hooves that rarely need protection at all.

I also have something to say to the veterinary community about natural hoof care. While the top researchers in the world are struggling to understand the complexities of laminitis and navicular syndrome, horse owners are curing hopeless navicular problems and coffin bone penetrations in their backyards.

How? By keeping their hooves well trimmed and attempting to provide a more natural lifestyle and diet for their horses. If the veterinary community will document some of these cases and do scientific research in the direction of natural hoof care we can be at the dawn of a new age of discovery. Too much research has been done on pathological hooves, while almost none has been done on truly healthy hooves. How can we possibly return pathological hooves to normal when so little is actually known about naturally healthy hooves? If we continue to consider a hoof that must be protected from contact with the ground by iron to be "normal", how can our studies on rehabilitation possibly be complete?

We must not allow ourselves to be isolated from each other and we must work at getting along and working together. Many times, I have heard people brag about how the vet and farrier were unable to do anything to help their chronic founder case, while the natural approach gave instant relief, then total cure. If we keep attacking others, we must expect them to fight back. We all need each other, and it's time for us to get together and figure out exactly what combinations of veterinary medicine, hoof care, and holistic care give the best results for a given hoof disorder. If we isolate ourselves from each other, we will *all* miss out and it is the horses who will suffer.

I, by no means, claim to know it all. I work hard to learn every day, and I can show you how to promote some amazing hoof healing. But I still need my vet, and the horses of the world need all farriers to understand as much as possible about their hooves. Let's get our heads together instead of bashing them against the wall.

Pete Ramey
Georgia/2003

Chapter 1
Our Model: the Natural Hoof

THE WILD HORSE HOOF

I cannot stress enough how important it is that every hoof practitioner study Jaime Jackson's wild horse research. This chapter is a tiny taste of it. Horses were born to travel twenty or more miles a day in harsh, varied terrain. This constant pounding tempers their hooves into a short, rock-hard piece of perfection that would delight any farrier, vet, or horse owner. This natural hoof is nature's intent and must be our model. Navicular syndrome, founder, white line disease, wall cracks, thrush, flaring and most other hoof disorders are almost never found in wild horse country, while the domestic hoof will almost always be plagued by several of these problems. The way we heal these problems is quite simple on the surface. We imitate the wild hooves as closely as possible with persistent trimming and try to provide a more natural diet and lifestyle.

The hoof in the picture at left belongs to an Appaloosa that can be ridden on any terrain. He works for a living in rugged mountain country and gets a light trim every four weeks. He is fast, agile, surefooted and always ready to go. He was given to us last year because his feet had been destroyed by a lifetime in a pasture without care. His hooves were flared and split to the hairline and were too far gone to shoe because the coffin bone was riding lower than any part of the hoof wall. Today they are sturdy and sound.

"Tough as steel" bare domestic hoof.

This is our goal with every hoof. Think about this: Nature did not create this remarkable animal and then put *anything* on the bottom of his foot that is not supposed to contact the ground! The frog, sole and bars, like the hoof wall, are all designed to withstand impact and constant contact with rough terrain.

The first step, then, is to know what is natural. We have been looking at hooves that have been spoiled by domestication for so long we need to take another look at what works best for the horse. The hooves should be short, with little or no hoof wall extending past the sole. The heels should be low. The sole should be concaved, and the frog should be like rawhide. The bars should gradually descend toward the wide frog, and the whole hoof should be free of splits, flaring and chips. There should be no deep, foul-smelling grooves, and the whole underside of the hoof should be tough and hard.

Sounds great, and most people would agree that this is an ideal hoof. The mistake people make is thinking we have "bred the hoof out of our horses." Nothing could be further from the truth. The hooves are only spoiled by inactivity, poor living conditions, soft ground, improper diet, and improper maintenance. Almost every domestic hoof can be transformed into what would be considered "genetic perfection." I'll show you how.

Here is a fine example. The horse on the left of this photo (*above*) is a former chronic founder case. When he was purchased by his current owner, she couldn't test ride him because he was almost immobile. She took me with her instead, and with my advice she got a real bargain in an incredibly athletic horse. He is as fast as greased lightning now and is completely sound on rough terrain. His white hooves are never chipped or split and there is always hoof wall to spare, in spite of the fact that he works for a living almost every day in rugged terrain. This is no fluke. The methods I will show you have been proven to me more times than I can count.

The fiery pinto on the left was a chronic founder case last year.

The Wild Horse Hoof

On this and following pages are pictures of an actual wild hoof. It has never been trimmed or altered in any way by a human. She was healthy and sound, but could not deal with captivity at all and was put down. This is the hoof that every horse was born to wear and will be a goal we will always gradually work our hooves toward.

This is our model. The closer I have managed to work horses toward it, the healthier and more able the horses become. Study these pictures carefully until they are burned into your brain. This is what is truly correct for the horse. If they look strange to you at first, you can be assured that it is because you are used to looking at very unnatural hooves that are so miserably sick that they must be protected from contact with the ground just to do the job they were created for.

Remember, though, that every hoof is an individual and that we do not force any ideal on them. Even in wild horse country, every hoof has its own individuality, but the same general shortness, health, and solar concavity are constant. Note the wide frog, and how flattened and firm it is (*left*). The heel bulbs are just as hardened and share a near seamless joint with the frog.

Note the perfect straightness of the hoof wall (*facing page*). There is no flaring. This is a work of art and a wonder of nature. Most wild hooves have toes that measure from 2⅝ to 3½ inches long, even on 1200 pound stallions. I have only come close to this appearance on one group of gaited horses, and this is because they are ridden barefoot around ninety miles a week at gait in very rough, mountainous country. As extreme as this sounds to most riders, this amount of movement is natural for horses, and that particular group is as sound and problem-free as any I have heard of anywhere.

For the most part, though, I have found that a 3 to 3½ inch toe is what I will wind up with on domestic horses ranging from 800 pounds to heavy drafts. I do not determine toe lengths, though. The hoof tells me its current

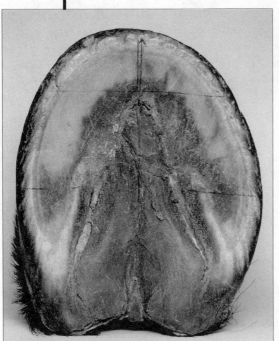

"Note the wide frog, and how flattened and firm it is. The heel bulbs are just as hardened and share a near seamless joint with the frog."

Making Natural Hoof Care Work for You

Wild horse hoof, left hind

"This is the hoof that every horse was born to wear and will be a goal we will always gradually work our hooves toward."

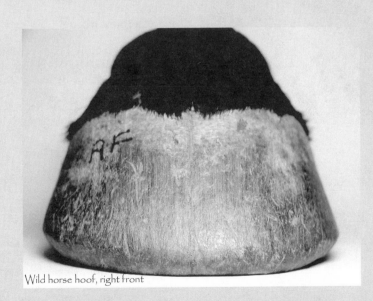

Wild horse hoof, right front

optimum length as I work it toward the model. I will explain that at length in the trimming chapters.

Take special note of the concavity of the hoof (*below*). It is important that you have a visualization of this because it will be very important to trimming. The concavity extends all the way to the hoof wall. The hoof wall stands only slightly above the sole and is never any longer than that. The hoof wall should not be forced to be flat like it is trimmed for shoeing but should be allowed to "hollow out" at the quarters like the arch of our own feet. This is natural, and our horses try to prove it to us every time they are turned out for a long period without maintenance. The quarters are the first area to break away. Shod horses will develop very thin hoof walls at the quarters because the hoof is resisting the unnatural level trimming and trying to adapt and remove the excessive hoof wall by producing a thinner hoof wall that would wear faster. Once the domestic horse begins a more natural hoof care program, he will immediately begin producing thicker hoof wall. It will be just as thick at the quarters as it is at the heel or toe just like a wild hoof.

"Take special note of the concavity of the hoof above. It is important that you have a visualization of this because it will be very important to trimming. The concavity extends all the way to the hoof wall."

There are mountains of information to learn from the wild ones. Study the beautifully rolled outer edge of the hoof wall. It extends all the way around the hoof and is an important part of natural hoof care. Few people realize that the hoof wall itself actually packs material into callous just like the sole and frog. Maintaining this "mustang roll", as we call it, promotes this callusing and keeps the hoof wall from splitting or fraying. Picture this: If you held a broomstick and started stabbing the rounded butt of it into gravel repeatedly, you can easily imagine that the round shape would be maintained as the stick wore down. Also, you can also probably visualize that

Making Natural Hoof Care Work for You

the rounded end would be packed into firmer material than the rest of the stick. It would take a very long time to wear that stick to a nub by stabbing it into the ground.

Now visualize breaking the rounded factory end off the broom. If you did the same stabbing into the ground with the split and tattered end, it would only make the splits and frays increasingly worse with every strike. It would not be very long until you ran out of stick. This is exactly how important the mustang roll is to hooves. In the wild, horses get enough movement on rugged terrain to maintain this shape themselves. Their domestic brothers who stand around all day in soft pastures will need our help.

This is a look inside another wild hoof (*right*). There is a lot going on here that no one on the planet fully understands. Study this cross section. Why is the hoof wall in this foot steeper than the coffin bone? How can a hoof be this short and still have deep solar concavity and a thick sole? How can the heels be so low that there are basically no heel bulbs whatsoever, yet the digital cushion and frog are thicker than in a domestic hoof? Is this coffin bone

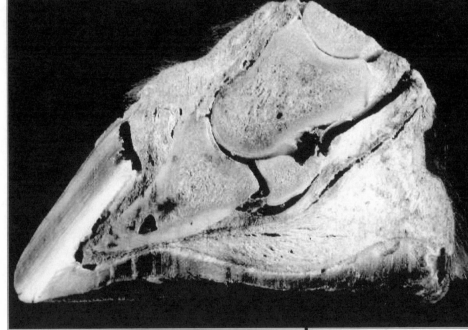

deformed, or is it normal and all of the domestic ones we have studied are deformed? Wild horses have an average life expectancy that more than doubles the average domestic horse and they do not founder, develop navicular syndrome, or have many of the other problems that plague the domestic horse. They are healthy, vibrant, and very capable. They are not troubled by parasites and maintain themselves without our help. This is not a separate species we are talking about. They are escaped domestic horses and their descendants. As soon as a wild horse is brought into captivity, all of his advantages are quickly stripped away. They are subject to all of the problems of domestication.

"This is a look inside another wild hoof. There is a lot going on here that no one on the planet fully understands."

To me, this does not sound like something the horse world should ignore. If we're so smart we should be able to provide care that is superior to no care at all; right? If you are reading this book, you probably love horses just as much as I do and I think we owe it to the horse to investigate his natural habitat a little. I know there are infinite answers waiting for us to discover. I have already seen what a relatively tiny amount of wild hoof study has done for thousands of horses, many of which had been declared incurably lame. As many research dollars that have gone into the horse, why has there been so little research done on it in his natural environment? When a zoo takes an animal out of the wild they must set up a habitat and diet that closely imitates its natural environment. Most horse owners don't have a clue what is natural for the horse. This would be the only sensible place to start, not only with their hooves but also with diet, exercise, training, and the list goes on. (Just think about how far horse training has come in recent years because a few people peeked into the natural horses' world.) Imagine the benefits our horses could reap if serious, scientifically controlled research were done.

I have heard it said many times that wild horses are so hearty because only the strong survive and weak animals are quickly turned into coyote bait. Certainly this is true and certainly we are allowing plenty of domestic specimens to survive that nature would have "culled out" in the wild, but think about this: *If nature does eliminate all of the horses with flawed hooves, then what is left in wild horse country?* That's right, the correct ones. This is precisely why we must study these hooves to learn what is truly right for the horse and in which direction we should work a flawed hoof.

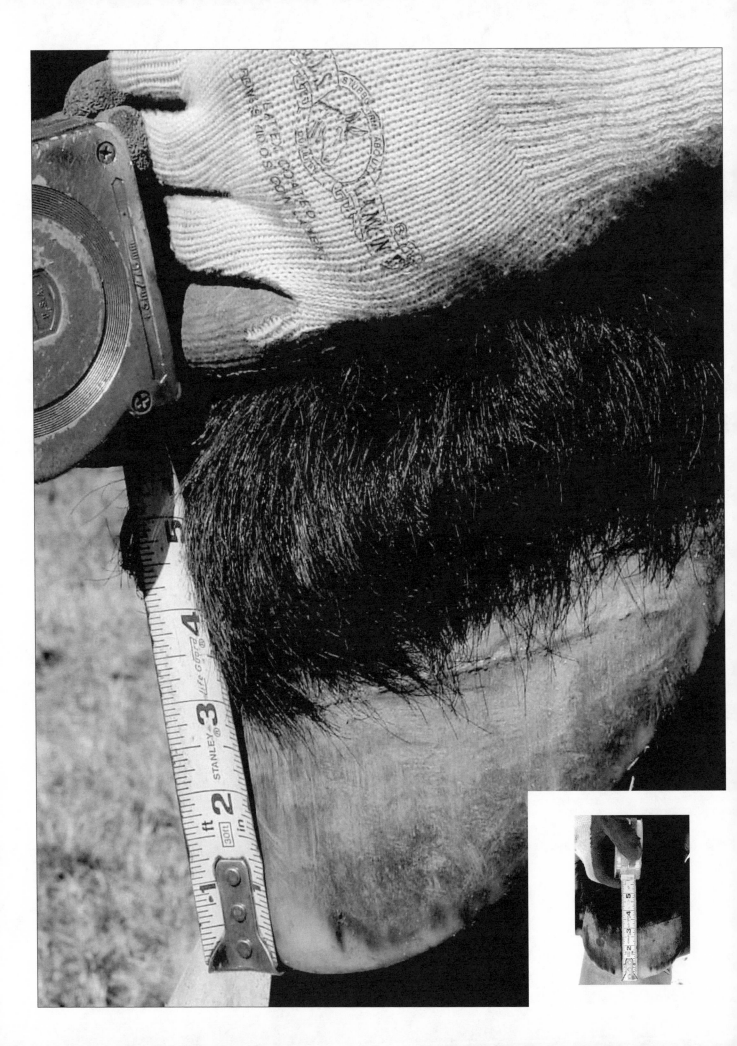

Chapter 2

The Domestic Hoof

HOOF x BREED

The Domestic Hoof

When a foal is born in the wild, it must be able to keep up with the herd almost immediately, and the hooves grow rapidly to accommodate this. That is why domestic foals' hooves get so long in a short period of time. Most people don't worry too much about this, but I can't stress enough how important it is to keep foal hooves in good shape. I have observed that it is only a matter of days before most foal's hooves are truly pathological when measured against the natural hoof and serious thought needs to be given to the early care of foals. When the heels get high, the coffin bone is standing on its sharp, pointed tip rather than having its solar surface parallel to the ground (or close to it) as nature intended (*left*). This puts unnatural stress on the lamina, and bone will start to sink lower into the hoof capsule and rotate away from the hoof wall. Also, if the heels remain low and the toe grows too long, the long lever created will pull the hoof wall up and away from the bone every time the hoof breaks over. Either way, the foal has just started out with a compromised hoof wall attachment, and the odds are it will be that

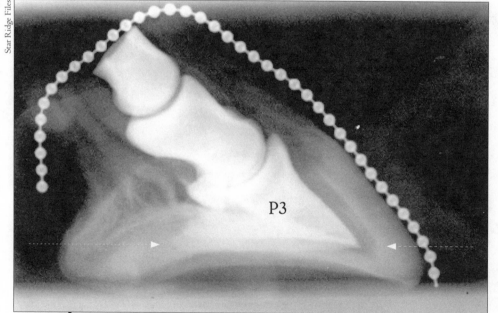

P3

"The coffin bone is basically shaped just like a miniature hoof. Nature intended it to be roughly parallel with the ground on the bottom."

Making Natural Hoof Care Work for You

way for the rest of his days. This is so common in the domestic horse, once you learn to recognize it and treat it, you will be well on your way to fixing most hoof ailments.

I'm talking about "coffin bone rotation," but that very term stops most hoof practitioners from being able to fix it or even being aware that it is possible to fix. The term suggests that the bone is trying to go somewhere when, in fact, it is right where it is supposed to be at the end of the skeleton. It's actually the hoof that has moved from its proper position around the bone. I use "hoof separation" instead in my everyday speech because the word "rotation" paralyzes horse owners with fear. Most people associate coffin bone rotation only with chronic laminitis but it is in fact very common in our everyday "sound" domestic horses. The notion that the rotation is being caused by the deep flexor tendon pulling the coffin bone out of place has led people to do the exact opposite of what needs to be done to stop it. All sorts of devices have been used to attempt to stop or reverse this rotation, but the reason they don't work is that they are simply trying to accomplish the impossible. Once the integrity of the lamina has been compromised, the *only* cure is to grow a new hoof that is well attached to the bone. We do this simply by identifying and removing the forces that are prying the hoof away.

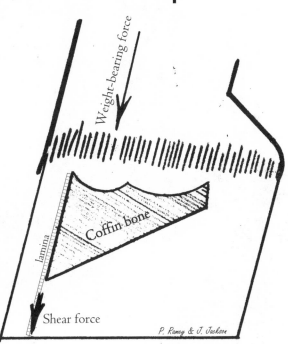

Dangerous unnatural forces caused by high (i.e., long) heels.

As you can see in the photo (*facing page*), the coffin bone is basically shaped just like a miniature hoof. Nature intended it to be roughly parallel with the ground on the bottom. When it is in this natural position, the impact forces are spread evenly around its entire surface. When the heels are high, the coffin bone is raised up on its tip. The wedge created by the pointed toe is driven downward with every step, tearing the lamina and separating the hoof wall from the coffin bone (*above*). The coffin bone is constantly being driven lower into the hoof capsule.

Unnatural forces per-
petuate flared toes.

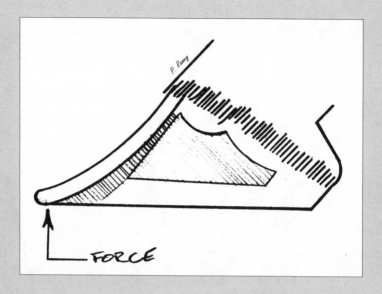

"When viewing a hoof
from the side, look at
the upper ½ inch of
hoof wall close to the
coronet band. If there
is a steeper angle at
the top, you can be
sure there is separation
present."

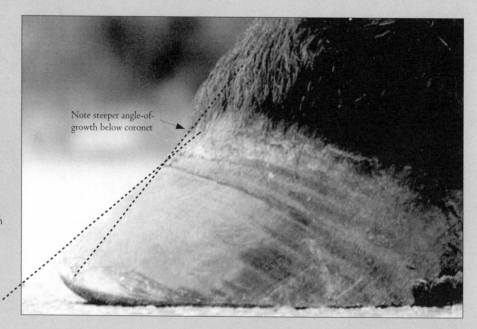

Note steeper angle-of-
growth below coronet

The other force behind rotation is a long toe (*top, facing page*). Once a toe gets stretched out in front of its natural position, upward force from the ground tears the lamina as well. High heels and long toes work together to constantly tear the hoof from its proper place as quickly as the horse can grow it.

When viewing a hoof from the side (*bottom, facing page*), look at the upper ½ inch of hoof wall close to the coronet band. If there is a steeper angle at the top, you can be sure there is separation present. This newly grown hoof wall shows us the natural angle for the horse, and that is what we must build on.

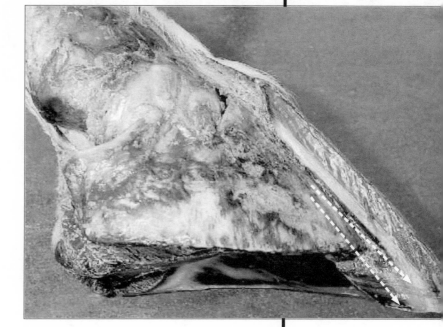

At right is a very informative view inside the hoof capsule. Note the slight flaring of the hoof wall away from the coffin bone. This is very minor, compared to the rotation I'm seeing on "sound" domestic horses everywhere. I've trimmed hooves all over the country, from marshlands to high desert, and it's the same story everywhere I go. Most practitioners and horse owners consider coffin bone rotation to be associated only with founder but it is actually so common it is impossible to isolate the teaching of healing of a chronic founder case from simply creating a sound barefoot horse with natural hooves. This is because a low or rotated coffin bone position (thus the "flat foot") is almost always the only thing causing a horse to "need" shoes. Luckily, this is easy to fix. This cross-section view of the hoof is not necessary to determine the coffin bone position. The trained eye will learn to "see" the coffin bone inside the hoof, and that is crucial to helping the horse grow his natural hoof – like those in the photos below.

The lamina joining the hoof wall to the coffin bone is similar to a piece of good cloth, in that it can be very tough to tear until a starting cut is made. It

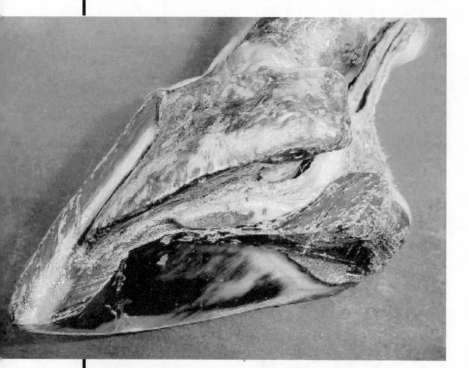

can then be easily ripped. Once the white line is compromised by separation, it can keep tearing, at least until the cause of the separation is determined and eliminated. This tearing is a constant source of pain. The more it tears, the further down the bone drops. This creates even more trouble because when the coffin bone loses its suspension in the hoof capsule, the horse is "flatfooted" and can go nowhere without hoof protection.

Below is the same hoof, tilted up slightly. As you can see, the solar (bottom) surface of the coffin bone is concaved. The sensitive corium and the sole follows this concavity, so we are able to concave the hoof without excessively thinning the sole. If the horse were moving twenty miles a day in wild horse country, he would wear this natural concavity himself, but this would be very rare in domestication.

The problem is that our horses have it too easy and that is the reason we must trim our horses. The goal of natural hoof care is to trick the hoof into "thinking" it is living on much harsher terrain than it really is. When a neglected hoof flares, chips and breaks, it is only attempting to adapt to its terrain and lifestyle. They usually remain sound, too, as long as they continue in the daily routine their hooves have adapted to. The problems don't begin until we try to ride them or work them on rougher terrain than their hooves are adapted to. Doing this without hoof protection would be cruel to say the least.

"Tricking" the hoof into adapting to the terrain we ride on rather than the terrain it lives on is the little piece of magic that natural hoof care is all about. Once competent natural trimming begins, the steeper hoof growth below the coronet will continue to grow in a straight line to the ground. The

"The same hoof, tilted up slightly. As you can see, the solar (bottom) surface of the coffin bone is concaved. The sensitive corium and the sole follows this concavity, so we are able to concave the hoof without excessively thinning the sole."

Making Natural Hoof Care Work for You

growth continues and the coffin bone will be lifted higher. Solar concavity forms as the bone moves higher off the ground, and the horse will become more able every day. Steady trimming activates growth, thickening and hardening just as hard wear would. This is how we work domestic hooves toward the model.

I would love to see radiographs of "newly rotated" foundered horses that were taken a week *before* the founder episode. I firmly believe it would be discovered that normally the rotation was not so sudden at all but a long-term problem that finally came to a head. The buildup of digestive toxins or perhaps excessive pounding on hard ground or simply time itself has manifested into sudden severe pain in *already* sick hooves. Many times I have been called out by the vet to a founder case only to look around and notice more coffin bone rotation present in the "sound" horses than in the "newly foundered" one. I have never seen or heard of a properly maintained horse with fully transitioned naturally shaped hooves founder, or develop any other hoof problems for that matter, not even once. It is time for the entire horse world to stand up and take notice.

Hoof x Breed

Natural hoof care works very well for all breeds. There are of course, differences in their hooves from one breed to the next, but following the same trimming parameters I will outline here and always aiming toward the wild model creates the best hoof for an individual breed, even though the end result may vary slightly from breed to breed.

I should point out here that draft horses take to natural hoof care exceptionally well. Their soles tend to remain a little flatter than smaller breeds, but they handle barefootedness very well if they are trimmed naturally and live in proper conditions. Draft horses are plagued with split hooves, since most owners tend to neglect them due to the price of draft shoeing. This doesn't have to be. Just take a look at the rock hard hooves of the draft horse grinding the pavement on the following pages.

(Continued on page 38)

This is a barefoot professional carriage horse working for a living on asphalt. Not only does he put out plenty of hoof growth to do the job, his previously flared, split hooves are continually improving as he works. His drivers report unbelievable traction, and that he is always fresh and raring to go at the end of the day, without the normal fatigue they have previously seen with shod horses. This is as extreme as it gets!

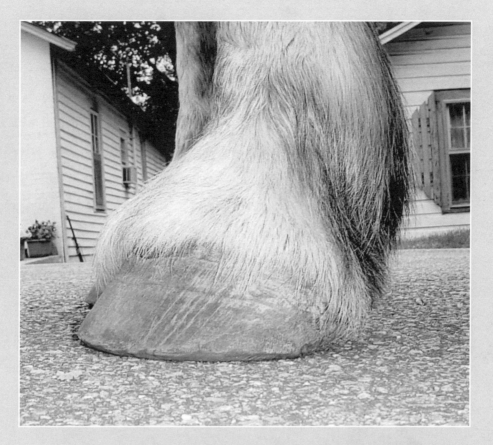

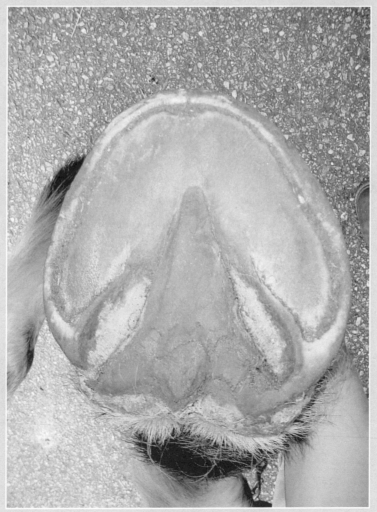

(Continued from page 35)

You haven't felt a smooth ride until you've been on a barefoot Tennessee Walker with naturally shaped bare hooves. I have heard owners of Missouri Fox Trotters and Paso Finos swear the same thing. They all maintain their gaits beautifully and move with maximum efficiency. In fact, these are the front hooves of a Missouri Fox Trotter fresh from a 200 mile week in some of Tennessee's rockiest mountain country (*below* and *facing page*). Almost all of this ride was at *gait* and all of it was barefoot. He is 100% sound and these pictures were taken *before* his maintenance trim right after he got back. What more could you ask for? In fact, this horse went on to become the World Champion in the Versatility Class . . . barefoot!

We are currently working out the details for an exciting new compromise for the owners of gaited show horses. It allows the horse to enjoy the health benefits of naturally shaped hooves while allowing the owners to enjoy the gait enhancement made possible by weighted shoes and wedge stacks. It involves making alterations to custom fitted hoof boots rather than to nailed-on horseshoes. The gait effects will not only be enhanced by the temporary nature of this system, it will be more readily adjustable. Imagine being able to make angle, weight, and position of weight adjustments in seconds for training and showing while the horse enjoys naturally shaped hooves during turnout.

I am convinced I could make a race horse run faster, and could of course keep it sound for much longer, but so far the opportunity has eluded me. It seems I keep repairing them *after* the track rather than before, but Thoroughbreds do extremely well barefoot and are especially thankful for the total end of under-run heels. A race horse raised with natural hooves would be a magnificent sight to behold. I have seen natural hoof care add speed, endurance, agility, and longevity to every breed under the sun. They make barrel horses sling dirt and increase traction beyond belief. The future of speed events is definitely back to nature as far as the hooves are concerned. Just wait and see.

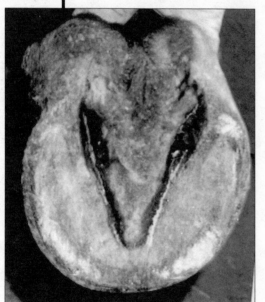

These are the front hooves of a Missouri Fox Trotter fresh from a 200 mile week in some of Tennessee's rockiest mountain country . . . He is 100%

(Continued on photo, facing page.)

I would be in favor of natural hoof care even if it meant changing the standards of competition. As I said earlier, I feel that harming the horse to boost performance is wrong and horses with bare natural hooves are much better off. The great part is that we *do not* have to sacrifice a thing because when properly trimmed and conditioned, a bare hoof performs better than a shod one. The reasons are simple. The added circulation gives the horse the feel for the ground that nature intended him to have and makes the horse more surefooted and less prone to injury. The natural hoof is deeply concaved but doesn't clog up with dirt, so every time it reaches for another stride it is like a clean shovel ready to dig. The short hoof and the lack of the added length of the shoe allow a smooth natural breakover which is far less stressful than anything you can achieve through shoeing. Without the shoe, there is less shock to be absorbed. So strain to the legs and back is much less and endurance is increased even with the added weight of the rider. I'm not trying to sell you a thing. You already have my book in your hand! I have watched the progress of thousands of horses and I am simply telling the truth. The first players in each area of competition to figure this out will be at an advantage until everyone else figures it out. Then all of the advantages will be for the horse.

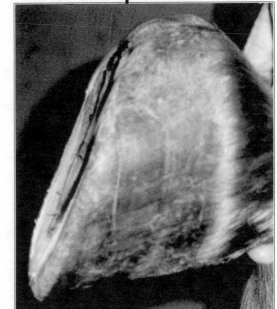

(Continued from photo, facing page)
sound and these pictures were taken *before* his maintenance trim right after he got back. This guy went on to win a world championship — barefoot!

Chapter 3
The Basic Natural Trim

The Basic Natural Trim

"A natural trim is
never invasive. ."

When trimming, always have goals in mind. Whether you are transitioning a sound, shod horse, or rehabilitating a chronic founder, always work toward the wild model. This does *not* mean that the hoof will be trimmed to imitate it completely. All horses were born to wear that foot but usually the unnatural lifestyle and care of domestication have already brought about changes in the hoof capsule. Most domestic hooves would be miserably lame and bleeding if they were cut that short at the first trimming. Natural trimming must be subjective because every hoof is different. This makes it complicated to learn. In the past (and present) trimming methods that enforce specific angles and dimensions on every hoof have been popular. Unfortunately, while this type of uniformity makes it easier for people to learn, it doesn't work very well for horses. You will have to learn to read the hoof. *A natural trim is never invasive.* If you ever draw blood while trimming a horse, you have not made a minor slip with your knife. You have made at least a $^3/_8$ inch mistake, and you need to seriously reevaluate where you are. It is natural for a horse to have around $^3/_8$ inch or more thick sole. *There is no excuse for invading this space unless you are a veterinarian performing a surgery.*

In this entire book you will find that I speak about rehabilitation as if it is a part of almost every trim. This is because almost every domestic hoof is in need of being rehabilitated to some degree. Even the very healthy barefoot hooves we are riding need to be continually worked toward the wild model. With the possible exception of true birth defects, every hoof was born to work hard without hoof protection. If later in life it cannot, there are specific reasons for it and most of them we can easily fix with natural care.

When I speak of general rehabilitation, I am grouping the chronically foundered horse, the everyday "flat footed" horse, the navicular horse, wall cracks, white line disease, horses with flared, weak, brittle or contracted hooves, faults in gait or movement of legs, and the "sound" horse that "just needs his shoes" in the same category because their rehabilitation needs are almost identical and all of them can have their tough, sound and naturally concaved hooves back if they receive proper care and lifestyle. I realize this sounds too simple on the surface, but there are some things you need to understand. The horse's entire locomotion system is on your side when you approach any hoof problem. The healing and adaptive abilities of the hoof are unbelievable. If you learn to read the adaptive attempt of the hoof, and remove excess the horse can't remove in captivity, the movement of the horse will make deeply complex changes that no one fully understands and forge the optimum hoof for the individual horse.

The two dimensional "corrective" decisions I used to make for hooves seem pitiful to me now when I compare them to the dramatic changes I watch hooves go through on their own now, with just a little simulation of natural wear. You're going to love this!

Trimming barefoot riding horses demands a higher level of intuition and competency. A horseshoe or a hoof boot can hide even the most serious errors in judgment (for a while). A mistake on a barefoot riding horse will tell on you in a heartbeat! This brutal honesty is what fascinates me so much and I wouldn't have it any other way. This is a big responsibility, though, so learn from what I have discovered and then use that foundation to learn even more. I am a serious student of the whole horse who spends a lot of time with a foot in my lap and I learn every day. Don't ever make the mistake of thinking you have mastered anything involving any living thing, but be careful where you learn from. Everyone has advice, so let the horse be the judge. If the individual horse is not making steady progress or is sore after your trim, you are probably making some mistakes!

I have taught many people to trim, and have watched other professional farriers and trimmers at work. *Most people make hoof trimming far more difficult than it should be.* It is human nature to want to fight and dominate, but let me tell you right now that there is no benefit to frightening the horse into submission. I promise that if you will just take the time to scratch the horse and buddy up with him before you begin, it will save time and sweat before the job is done. Be sure that he is balanced before asking for a hoof. Avoid crossties. Above all, work where the horse is comfortable. Many times I have seen a "difficult" horse become a pussycat, simply by leading it over to its buddy and working there.

As a professional, a big advantage to natural hoof care over shoeing is that you are so portable. I have a truck full of junk, for some unknown reason, but day to day all I need are my chaps, rasp, knife, and nippers. I get under a shade tree in the pasture and don't even bother to go to the barn. This method has an extraordinary calming effect over dragging the horses one by one to the farrier's truck, and it's a very pleasant way to spend a day.

I try to regulate my customers to steady four to six week trimming schedules, although some horses can go longer. Four week schedules are best though for inexperienced trimmers, horses in rehabilitation, and heavily used horses at work or training — so four week intervals should actually be our standard. If you wait until the hoof "looks bad" to trim, you have done damage. We must trim *before* damage is done. This seems to be one of the most critical elements of natural hoof care, and people not willing to steadily maintain their hooves are wasting their time reading this book. The hoof is highly adaptive and when it gets too long, whether because of a shoe or neglect, it immediately starts to prevent and attempt to remove excess growth. It does this in several ways. Hoof production is slowed down considerably, and a thinner and considerably weaker hoof horn will be produced. The sole, which should be slick and hard as a rock turns into flaky, chalky material that can be scraped away with a hoof pick.

When the hoof is steadily kept at a natural length, the opposite happens. From the beginning you can see a tougher, healthier horn growing from the coronet. When it reaches the ground it is often twice the thickness it was in the beginning. Hoof production speeds up dramatically. I have observed working horses growing new hooves from the hairline to the ground in less than five months. This adaptation is what keeps the horse's hooves correct in the wild. Our horses would do it on their own too, *if* they were living the life-style they were created for. The bottom line is that you can make some mistakes in your trimming but don't make the mistake of not doing it. The reward is a horse that is faster and more agile, with smoother gaits and more endurance. It will be highly resistant to most lameness and will probably be with you for many extra years.

Getting Started

The first step in trimming is to place the horse on a level surface, stand back and observe. Note any imbalance. Take note of any flaring of the hoof wall. Flaring simply reveals past or present excessive length and is a serious weakness. It will be a major priority when trimming. Viewing the hoof from the sides, note the toe wall. Is it straight from the hairline to the ground or does the angle change. Try to visualize the coffin bone as discussed earlier. If you work toward being able to plan your entire trim with a glance at the hoof on the ground, it will save time and effort.

Don't let pastern angles or their relationship to the hoof angle influence hoof trimming. In my shoeing days I was taught to try to set the hoof angle to the pastern and shoulder angles, but this is incorrect. Sometimes an "upright" horse is being forced into that conformation by unnatural hooves. If the individual horse really is genetically steep and in need of a more upright hoof, the clues I will teach you will show you the perfect hoof for the existing conditions with the individual horse.

Horses with heel pain will tend to "lean forward" and toe pain causes them to "lean back." This has a dramatic effect on the hoof/pastern relationship, as can muscular or skeletal problems. All of this can play tricks on your mind and attempting to force the hoof and pastern angles to match becomes a real joke if you try to be truly particular about it. What I *have* found is that a horse that has grown his optimum hoof and is free of any pain will wind up with a perfect hoof/pastern relationship almost every time. I agree that it is correct for the angles to line up. I simply know from experience that it is a terrible idea to alter the hoof from its natural form based on the pastern angles.

In the past, I determined hoof angles and heel heights by judging conformation of the horse. My experience with natural hoof care has taught me that by judging and trimming the hoof by coffin bone position only, and using the methods of hoof reading I will describe, you will grow the horse's perfect hoof and the healing powers through the entire body are extraordinary. "Which comes first, the chicken or the egg?" I simply think that deviating from the *model* to compensate for another defect is a mistake. It tends to perpetuate the problem rather than aiding the horse in any way. So at least we have one consistency in our life; we *always* work towards the natural model. We definitely do not ignore the conformation of the horse; we just allow natural adaptation to create the perfect support and rehabilitation shape for the hoof. It may shock you to learn that if you listen, the hoof itself will tell you everything you need to know. I will show you how to read the adaptive attempts by the horse and by simply removing the excess growth and respecting this adaptation, the horse's own movement will forge the exact hoof that it needs to not only be sound on his own bare feet, but heal almost any locomotion ailment you have ever heard of.

I have heard all sorts of justifications for altering the hoof from its natural form. Every time someone decides to let a toe or heel grow long to create a "desired" effect on the gait of a horse, they are committing the sin of sacrificing the health of the animal to accommodate the desires of the human. I am sick of seeing horses treated as disposable items. The destructive stresses caused by long toes and high heels are well documented in every equine veterinary text I have seen, but still people persist. Do you really think it is okay for your horse to have a short career just because everyone else in your field of competition has the same problem? It is natural for horses to be absolutely at their athletic prime through their late teens. If your particular competitive

Making Natural Hoof Care Work for You

field considers it normal for a horse's career to be two or three years, I would suggest the methods and parameters of competition, training and care be seriously reevaluated. Who do we think we are?

I trim every hoof with the natural model in mind, yet in this book you will see trimmed hooves with heel lengths ranging from nonexistent to almost an inch long. You may or may not be able to pinpoint exactly *why* an individual horse has a specific trimming need, but I can teach you exactly how to determine *what* the hoof needs to do the maximum benefit to the horse while remaining sound.

I will discuss each part of the hoof in detail in the order I evaluate and trim them myself. *The most common mistake I see, is trimming the hoof from the outside – in.* It is crucial that you learn to visualize the coffin bone position and thus the true shape and form of the individual horse's natural hoof. The upper inch or so of newly grown hoof wall will show you the direction the hoof needs to grow. The sole will tell you more than anything you can see from the top about the height of the suspension of the coffin bone relative to the hoof capsule. Understanding this will be the most useful tool in determining how quickly the horse will have tough, healthy hooves.

The Sole Callus

The sole has been ignored by farriers and trimmers for long enough. Everyone seems to have their idea of how hooves should be trimmed and the sole is treated as an idle passenger. If you will learn to use the sole itself as *the* primary guide to hoof trimming, you will be able to amaze everyone around you with your sound, free moving barefoot horses and your uncanny ability to solve almost any hoof or locomotion problem. The outer band of sole approximately one inch wide (in a 1000 pound horse and varying proportionally with different hoof sizes) is an important area we must trim as little as

> "The most common mistake I see, is trimming the hoof from the outside – in. It is crucial that you learn to visualize the coffin bone position and thus the true shape and form of the individual horse's natural hoof. The upper inch or so of newly grown hoof wall will show you the direction the hoof needs to grow."

possible (*sketch below*). It runs from bar to bar adjacent to the white line all the way around the hoof. I usually trim the dead sole from this area the *first* time I trim a horse that has been shod because I usually find the overall hoof to be too long. After that day, I almost never touch a tool to that area again. The sole (as well as the hoof wall and frog) packs into denser, tougher material as it continually pounds on the ground. If the horse is left barefoot and 24 hour turnout is provided, the sole will not build up in soft flaky layers as we are accustomed to seeing with shod horses, but will harden off and start to concave itself immediately.

Any trimming method that prescribes a routine removal of the hard, calloused sole in this area stands between the horse and soundness. Any corrective measure that involves either trimming into quality sole or building above it defies everything that the natural healing abilities of the horse are trying to accomplish, and you *will* ultimately fail.

That is a promise. This callous is crucial and we manage it by doing what we can to ensure it receives as much passive wear as possible so that we will not need to trim it. We do this by the following:

1) Never let excessive hoof wall build up. Among many other problems, a long hoof wall protects the sole from the wear that is essential to callusing. If the hoof wall grows long the sole horn will pile up in flakes rather than packing into slick, hard callous. This is similar in effect to wearing a horseshoe.

2) Never let the bars grow excessively long. Long bars provide excessive protection just like a long hoof wall. I will describe proper bar trimming later in this chapter.

3) Allow plenty of movement.

Remember our goal is to trick the hoof into adapting to a harsher envi-

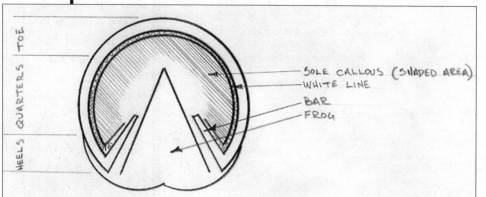

"The outer band of sole approximately one inch wide (in a 1000 pound horse and varying proportionally with different hoof sizes) is an important area we must trim as little as possible."

Making Natural Hoof Care Work for You

ronment than it actually lives on. If the horse was actually in the wild and was getting the 20 miles per day of movement on rough, varied terrain as nature intended, he would need the rapid growth of the hoof wall and bars to protect the sole from excessive wear. In domestication this same protection works against us in a way by allowing the sole to become too soft. It is ironic that the key to creating a rock crushing barefoot horse is to actually keep its own defenses in check!

The reward is a slick, shiny, calloused sole that immediately starts to concave itself more every day, in spite of (actually because of) the fact that no one is cutting it. The deeply concaved, thick sole of the wild model is natural for the horse and even the most hopelessly "flatfooted" domestic hoof will return to it as soon as you let it.

The sole callous lies directly beneath the coffin bone, and in horses with poor or no coffin bone/hoof wall attachment, allowing callous buildup is critical to the horse's comfort during rehabilitation. As we grow our firmly connected hoof capsule and the coffin bone is suspended higher off the ground, the flat area of the sole callous will disappear and the sole will concave itself.

Leaving this area alone will seem like an impossibility at first to farriers. Most will visualize the result being long, stretched out toes. The opposite is true and I will explain this at length in the *toe* section. Every single horse in my care (with the exception of a *small* percentage of the draft horses) has a toe length under 3½ inches and a short natural breakover. Rasping the sole at the toe is probably the most common (and serious) mistake by farriers and carving away the sole at the heels and quarters is the most common and serious mistake of barefoot trimmers. If it seems necessary on an individual hoof it is very likely you are misreading the situation. I will explain later how solar concavity must be *built — not cut.* The sole callous and its management are first in this chapter for a reason. It is the most important ingredient and a well calloused sole should be your top priority.

Roughing Out the Hoof

With the hoof knife, scrape away any loose, crumbly sole from the bottom of the hoof. Anything that is loose, crumbly or foul should be removed first. On a shod horse, there will most likely be plenty of crumbly sole to remove, and probably little or none on a horse that has been barefoot. It is always okay to remove powdery sole, as it is definitely old sole the horse is attempting to remove himself. Stop when you get to firm, quality sole. Clean all the way to the hoof wall, leaving it standing alone for removal.

Hoof wall standing alone above the sole wears or breaks away easily, much like a fingernail that grows long past the finger. *When the horse turns live sole into flaky, powdery material it is actually trying to remove hoof wall in that area.* If the horse was getting the amount of movement on rough terrain that his feet were designed for, the hoof wall would wear away as the live sole was removed by the horse. This is the single most important clue we have in determining what a hoof needs us to trim and the reading of these adaptation attempts should carry a lot of weight in any trimming decision you make. The more I have learned to respect this rather than my own ideas and what I have read or been told, the more able my horses have become.

With nippers, rasp, or hoof knife, trim the hoof wall all the way around. Cut only the hoof wall standing above the firm sole. Leave the hoof wall standing $1/16$ inch above the sole. This step will be pretty much eliminated after the first trimming because hopefully we won't allow the hoof to overgrow again.

> "When the horse turns live sole into flaky, powdery material it is actually trying to remove hoof wall in that area."

Frog/Sole Juncture (Collateral Grooves)

Looking at the bottom of the hoof, the grooves that follow the sides of the frog where you normally would run a hoof pick are our best indicator of coffin bone position and thus, are the best indicator of where the horse's optimum hoof should be. It tells us exactly how deep the hoof can be concaved, and how long the toe and heels should be trimmed. The wild model is always our ultimate goal, but we have to get there by respecting the current conditions and aiming in the direction of the wild model rather than hacking the hoof to it on day one. Understanding that the frog/sole juncture is the absolute limit of any trimming will help keep you from trimming a hoof too low for the existing conditions within the hoof capsule.

Along the sides of the frog there is a "seam" between the sole and frog. After trimming away the "flaps" or folded over sides of the frog it will be visible as a thin hairline of dirt between the frog and sole. The very bottom of this crevice is the frog/sole juncture. Never trim *any* lower than this, as it represents the lowest point of concavity of the sole and frog. Everything flows up and out from there.

Don't forget that the underside of the coffin bone is very concaved, and that the corium (quick) follows it. Any sole or frog trimming must flow up and out from the frog/sole juncture (when I say "up" I am speaking from the trimmer's perspective with the hoof tilted upside down).

It is *very* important to note that we will not trim the sole all the way to the frog/sole juncture, but it is important to know where the *bottom* is when faced with a truly overgrown hoof. If at any point during trimming the seam of dirt between the sole and the frog disappears, that means, "Don't go any deeper." Experience will teach you when the seam is about to disappear, but meanwhile it is okay to carefully trim sole and frog at the apex (tip) of the frog only, until the seam just disappears, so you can use that point as a reference.

The trimming of the concavity of the sole is the most intimidating part of a natural trim at first, and it should be. It requires judgment and experience to get it right, and its description is the toughest part of writing this book. It also is the key element to enabling the horse to be a gravel-crunching, high performance barefoot horse, so work hard at mastering this. It is critical for expansion, and thus blood flow and shock absorption. I wish I could lay out a formula of some kind for you to trim by, but you're stuck with only judgment. What I *can* do is help you figure it out a whole lot quicker than I did. (The **Resource** section of this book will show you how to contact a competent professional in your area.)

> "The trimming of the concavity of the sole is the most intimidating part of a natural trim at first, and it should be."

Study the wild hoof pictures in this book and get an image in your mind of natural concavity. That bowl you will start to see in your head must flow up from the bottom of the frog-sole juncture in the front half of the frog forward of the bars. What makes this so tough for people to get right is that in the hoof with a low coffin bone position, which is *far* more common than the healthy one, the coffin bone is positioned too close to the ground. This means that the hoof will not be capable of being concaved all the way *to the hoof wall* yet. In this "flat foot" if you set the hoof knife at the angle of the natural concavity of the wild model and trim the ridge of sole immediately adjacent to the frog like hollowing out a bowl, the trim will *not* extend all the way out to the hoof wall at the quarters or toe if there is not enough available depth! In the future it will, but in the beginning the sole is usually too thin. It must be left alone and allowed to build. As I mentioned earlier, the outer majority of the sole will maintain and concave itself readily, if the bars and the ridge of sole adjacent to the frog are kept in check.

The most common way that beginners and misguided professionals sore horses is by a lack of understanding this. They will keep concaving the sole in areas where it is already too short. It would be *far* better to leave the sole alone completely than to cut too much, but mastering the sole is worth the trouble, because this speeds up transition time dramatically, and boosts performance. Please read this section over and over until you understand every word. This is critical. The bowl is the vision in your mind of the concavity of a wild hoof. The bottom of the frog-sole juncture forward of the bars is the bottom of the bowl. The deeper it is, the wider it reaches toward the hoof wall. If it is shallow it will not reach far from the frog and the remaining sole between the cut and the hoof wall will be left alone to grow thicker and more concaved. *After the first trim you will almost never cut the sole except in a ¾ inch band around the frog forward of the bars.*

The following sketches will demonstrate the importance of the frog/sole juncture to trimming (*facing page*). They represent a cross section of the hoof viewed from the front, and cut about a half inch behind the point of the frog. Note that in the top sketch the coffin bone is suspended well off the ground,

> "After the first trim you will almost never cut the sole except in a ¾ inch band around the frog forward of the bars."

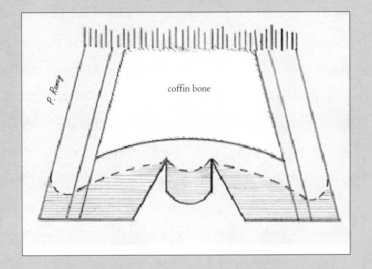

coffin bone

P. Ramey

"The hoof can be safely trimmed along the dashed line and all of the shaded area is excess which should be removed."

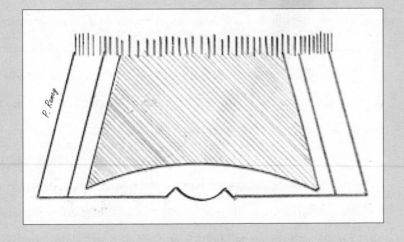

P. Ramey

The coffin bone has become too low in the capsule, and thus the hoof has become a "flat foot" and the evidence that shows us this is the depth of the frog/sole juncture. The hoof can be safely trimmed along the dashed line and all of the shaded area is excess which should be removed. Again, always let caution and common sense be the ultimate guide. Don't cut through the live, healthy sole to achieve *any* goal.

In the lower sketch (*previous page*), the hoof may have a similar look at first glance, but the shallow frog/sole juncture reveals that this hoof cannot be concaved very deeply. This the most critical section in this book, so slow down and soak this in because this is the typical "sound" domestic horse that "just needs his shoes". If I've heard it once, I've heard it a thousand times: "The flatfooted horse is a genetic flaw." *Wrong!* It is caused mostly by the long term effects of sole trimming by farriers and barefoot trimmers. [I am also finding that the roots of "flat-footedness" and also every other domestic hoof problem lie in the early neglect of foal hooves, and the lack of natural miles domestic foals travel. As more research is done, I am confident that this will be found to be of major importance.]

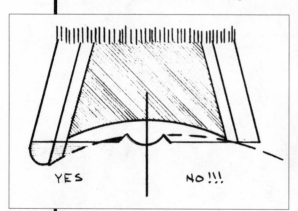

Correct and incorrect methods of achieving a concaved sole.

The dashed line at the right of the sketch at left shows the number one error I am seeing barefoot trimmers make. The shallow dirt line shows us that the coffin bone is too close to the ground and thus the sole at the quarters (or anywhere else) is too thin. Don't trim an area you should be building up! Instead, trim the sole close to the frog as represented by the dashed line on the left of the sketch and allow the shaded area to fill in over time.

It is very interesting to note that as this increased sole builds at the quarters, the hoof itself does *not* get longer as the sketch suggests. Instead, the building sole drives the coffin bone and thus the solar dome higher in the hoof capsule and the overall hoof length actually gets *shorter* over time in most cases as concavity of the sole increases. This is probably the single most important observation I have made. The "flip-side" of that reasoning is that the trimming away of the sole in the entire area under the coffin bone by farriers and misguided trimmers is the precise mistake that leads to the low cof-

Making Natural Hoof Care Work for You

fin bone position in most domestic hoof capsules. An understanding of this will make you able to easily give almost any horse tough, natural hooves. *Solar concavity must be built, not cut.*

I am stressing this now, and I will stress it again because this is the most important finding that has led me to success with natural hoof care.

Heels and Bars

Again, our desired heel length is that of the natural model, which is extremely short but thick and tough. *We absolutely must not sore the horse in the name of rehabilitation, because the most important aspect of rehabilitating anything on the horse is movement. Any trimming method that prescribes trimming horses in such a way that they are less comfortable after the trim is inherently wrong.*

That said, we do want to get the heels as low as possible and we want to keep them there, because this is what the wild hooves show us to be natural. As healing takes place within the hoof the heels will widen, the sensitive tissues will move up, and you will be able to work the heel lower and lower until it gets to its optimum position. Problems with an individual horse may cause it to continue keeping a higher than natural heel on one or more feet, but keeping them as low as possible without invading the proper sole thickness will give the horse the best help for the hooves and for the rest of the body.

The best I can calculate through dissections and experience is that the sole should be at least $^3/_8$ inch thick everywhere. If it gets thinner, the horse will be sore footed and if it gets thicker, the hoof is too long and is subject to the problems already discussed. Skill at walking this tightrope is what separates the masters from the hackers in hoof trimming.

Look at the back of the heel. There is a "V" between the origin of the frog and the origin of the heel on each side of the frog. It is the widest point of the frog. 90% of the time I wind up trimming the heels ¼ to ½ inch long measured from the very bottom of this "V" during the first trim. That sounds easy enough doesn't it? What complicates heel trimming is that if I trimmed *all* of

> We absolutely must not sore the horse in the name of rehabilitation, because the most important aspect of rehabilitating anything on the horse is movement. Any trimming method that prescribes trimming horses in such a way that they are less comfortable after the trim is inherently wrong.

my customers' heels to that level during the first trim, the other 10% would be sore or damaged, and I would have been run out of town or worse years ago! Thus, the level we will cut heels is a complex subject we simply cannot apply a measurement to.

As I have repeated throughout this book, every horse was born to wear the low, strong heel of the wild model, but through unnatural trimming and living conditions, the coffin bone actually sinks lower in the hoof capsule than it should be, taking the live corium at the heel with it. This means that usually we cannot lower the heel as far as we would like and still maintain the $^3/_8$ inch thick sole, and there is not a firm heel height that is right for all horses. With consistent trimming or wear, the bone and thus the corium are somehow pushed back up in the hoof capsule. Understanding of this phenomenon would help us understand why a wild hoof averages almost a full inch shorter than the hooves of most domestic horses the same size.

I will cut a two inch heel off of a horse in a heartbeat *if* the conditions in the hoof are present that demonstrate that the horse is trying to remove it, and doing so can turn a sore, short-striding, upright horse into a vision of health immediately. After thousands of trims, I have never seen any tendon or muscular problems from this as some might suspect, only dramatic improvement. This is because once you learn to read the hoof, it will tell you the truth.

The hoof will never develop the conditions that tell us we can lower a heel if the tendons, ligaments and muscles are not in need of it. If, however, the conditions are not right in the hoof, *cutting a long heel off in one session can be devastating to the horse so never trim this dramatically unless you are absolutely positive the horse is in need of it*. It is always safer to make changes over time. No human has enough knowledge to determine which is right in a given situation, but the hoof itself can show you the right answer. This is how simply paying attention to the condition of the sole will keep you out of trouble.

Don't let an under-run heel fool you. Sometimes, particularly with thoroughbreds and draft horses, the heel grows forward, rather than down. The

Cutting a long heel off in one session can be *devastating* to the horse so never trim this dramatically unless you are absolutely positive the horse is in need of it.

Making Natural Hoof Care Work for You

base of support moves forward and the destructive powers are devastating to the horse. This is usually initially caused by the quarters being left too long, and it is worse than high heels for the horse, by far. When the hoof is rasped flat for a horseshoe, the hoof wall at the quarters are longer than what is natural. This tends to drive the coronet upward, causing a high bulge in the hairline above the quarters when the hoof is viewed from the side. This in turn causes the coronet to approach the heel perpendicular to the ground, causing the heel to grow forward rather than down. I should stress here that I am not a proponent of any attempts to force the hairline to be perfectly straight, as the wild hooves prove that a slight dome in the hairline is natural. It is, however, important to note that excessive distortions in the hairline can point you to serious long term trimming problems. Never leave a long under run heel on a horse, avoid rasping the hoof "flat," and under-run heels will quickly be eliminated.

So how do you know how far to lower a heel? Start by scraping away any flaking or loose sole material in the seat of corn area which lies in the "V" between the hoof wall and the bars. Dig out this "chalk" all the way until you get to firm sole. The heel and bar left standing alone above the firm sole can be cut away for sure because this loose sole material shows us that the hoof is trying to remove that area anyway. That is "listening" to the hoof and is very important. Trim away this excess, balancing the heel by gauging the distance from the hairline on each side. This is where you should stop. This will maximize the horse's comfort. The next time you trim, if the heels need to come on down there will be chalky sole in the corn area to guide you. If not, there will be calloused sole there.

It is important that you understand this. *It has been a common mistake to routinely lower heels past the point where the sole at the heel (seat-of-corn) is firm and healthy.* I used to do it too, and have found it to be a fundamental mistake. The problem with this is that somehow this loss of live sole registers to the hoof as excessive wear, or literally as a wound, and it is quickly reqrown. If you have ever fought to keep a heel low as I did in the past, you know what I mean. What I have discovered is that if you leave the calloused sole at the heel alone and routinely lower any hoof wall standing above the sole, the heel will retreat on its own (if and when it needs to). This way, you get your low heel *and* the tough calloused sole. It is my theory that the "mysterious" force that drives the corium upward is the calloused sole itself, and all this time we have been rasping away at heels, we have been working against the horse. If we only remove the excess hoof wall the heel quickly adapts to its optimum height. If this seems impossible, try it before you knock it. I am getting heels lower than I ever have, now, by doing this, and never have a horse sore after a trim.

The distance from the ground to the coronet at the heel should match on each side of the foot. If one bulb is pushed up higher than the other, still gauge each heel length from its respective hairline and match the distances on each side. The bulbs will usually level out almost immediately after the horse has a chance to move around. The exception to this, of course, is if making both heels the same length from the hairline would cause you to invade the live sole. Go as far as the heel will allow, and work it down each trim. This is rare; usually you will be able to get the heels and bulbs balanced on the first trimming, even in the most dramatic cases, because the hoof will already be attempting to return to this correct position by removing firm sole on the high side.

The bars have been a major arguing point. Are they supposed to support weight or not? Both sides are right and wrong. The wild model gives us the answer. The bars are, in fact, supposed to carry a share of the load, as is everything else on the bottom of the foot, but they are supposed to carry only a "passive" load. This means that they should *never* be allowed to reach the same length as the main hoof wall, but they can't be gouged out either. They should, however, stand slightly ($1/16$ inch) above the concaved sole that lies adjacent to them and extending towards the seats-of-corn (turn of the hoof wall at the heel-buttresses). Trim the bars so that they descend toward the frog in a straight line. They should originate at the level of the heel and follow the level of, or standing slightly above, the firm, quality sole (after any dead or loose sole has been cleaned out, of course). If the bar is bent or laid over unnaturally, don't let this influence you to cut deeper. Follow these same parameters and the bar will become straight in time and the horse will be comfortable while you wait.

A bent or "laid over" bar is no different than a flare in the outer hoof wall. It can't perform the support role it was designed for and needs to be straightened. However the practice of hacking away at the bar until it is straight is no different than performing a resection on a hoof just to get rid of a simple flare. On the flip-side of that, if you continue to leave the flared bar level with the hoof wall, it will never straighten or be capable of providing the support nature intended. The answer to the problem lies in simply consistently maintaining the bars as described above. They will straighten out soon enough.

As I mentioned earlier, a ridge of sole that extends from the bar and follows the frog will form. *As you trim the bar, extend the cut along sides of the frog and around the apex so that the line of the hoof's natural concavity extends to the frog.* This corresponds to the dashed line in the figure at right. Do not allow this cut to go deeper than the frog/sole juncture. It is my theory that this ridge of sole returns to give extra resistance to wear at the center of the hoof. The wild hooves show us that the hoof does not crave a "pillar" in the center of the foot, so this extra sole growth must be necessary to protect the sole from excessive wear. In our "sedentary" domestic horses, we must help the hoof adapt by keeping this ridge in check. This allows the rest of the sole to receive enough wear to form good callous.

An exception I have found should be noted. Thoroughbreds living and working on sandy footing often need this ridge and the bars left alone, even to the point of being as high as the plane of the hoof wall. I cannot explain this, except that perhaps the protruding bar compensates for the unnatural footing by increasing pressure there. I greatly increased the soundness and performance of my jumpers when I figured this out. I was finding the severely protruding bars and adjacent sole ridge on most of them at each trim, and

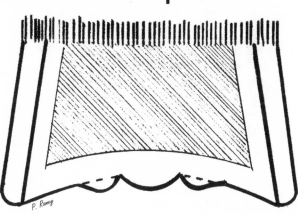

P. Ramey

"As you trim the bar, extend the cut along sides of the frog and around the apex so that the line of the hoof's natural concavity extends to the frog."

was habitually removing it. It bothered me that the sole ridge was so firm, alive, and seemed to pop back quickly when removed. (All of which are big red flags that you are making a major trimming mistake.) Also, some of my Thoroughbreds would be sore after a trim, which is of course unacceptable. When I started experimenting with leaving this ridge along the frog alone, the results were spectacular. This would cause troubles if the horse was occasionally ridden barefoot in rough terrain, so I recommend boots for this just to be on the safe side. *The bottom line is to always listen to the horse and never accept soreness caused by a trim. Always be willing to adapt your ideals to the individual situation and your abilities will continue to improve.*

It would undoubtedly be even better if we did not have to cut this area of sole either, but I have found this to be a very comfortable (for the horse) compromise, as callusing the outer band of sole under the coffin bone seems to be far more critical to soundness as it receives more abuse. Keeping the ridge along the frog in check will allow the outer band of sole to callous and concave itself without our touching a tool to it.

So always it is the firm, callused, outer band of sole adjacent to the hoof wall that we trust as a guide over everything else. After the initial set-up trim, if you steadily remove any flaking sole material and any hoof wall standing above the firm sole, the horse will adapt towards his optimum hoof on his own, without becoming sore. The more often you remove this excess and the more exercise the horse gets the quicker the progress will be. As time goes by and the optimum form is reached the flaking will stop and the sole will harden off. If the horse has physical problems that warrant a longer heel the sole will not become flaky in that area. If this is the case, respect this need that the horse is showing you. The adaptive powers of the natural hoof "know" what the horse needs more than any human can calculate. The horse only needs to have the excess hoof wall taken away as it weakens the adjacent sole for removal. *Think of trimming as a process, rather than a cutting to a particular dimension.* We are only enabling the horse to do what nature intended, and this is exactly how such a simple method rehabilitates so many problems and sets the horse up perfectly for its individual environment and breed.

> "The bottom line is to always listen to the horse and never accept soreness caused by a trim. Always be willing to adapt your ideals to the individual situation and your abilities will continue to improve."

> "Think of trimming as a process, rather than a cutting to a particular dimension."

The *only* time you should trim into live sole at the heels to speed up the process of heel lowering is when the horse is in pain that is being caused by the high or under run heel. An example of this is with a rotating coffin bone in a foundered horse. If high heels are present, the coffin bone will be standing too vertically and the pointed tip is pushing its way toward the ground. Rapid heel reduction removes this force, stopping the rotation or sinking. I normally lower heels to the widest point of the frog in this case (more about this later). This is usually a dramatic pain reliever, but it is crucial that you not make the heels sore, as this would leave the horse with no comfortable place to stand. This should be considered an extreme measure for an extreme situation. The rest of the time, don't be in a hurry to get the heels lowered. The very quickest way to get the hooves in their optimum state is to keep him comfortable and moving as much as possible and this means we will never risk making a sound horse uncomfortable by forcing our goals upon it. If you see one speck of blood you overdid it. If the heels get sore you went too far. It's not the end of the world, however. It will grow right back. Apologize to the horse, don't charge the owner, and learn something from your mistake.

Don't let bruising scare you away, though. It has been my observation that excessive sole is by far the most common cause of sole bruises and if you trim hooves you will see bruising. Most people will be very surprised to find that you will almost always find sole bruising on the first trim of a shod hoof and almost *never* see it once the horse has been barefoot under natural care. It is a major mistake to shy away from cutting a bruised area of sole (or frog) because you will wind up leaving the one sore spot on the sole or frog standing higher, causing more pressure to be put on it. "Quicking" a horse comes without warning (other than softness of the sole). The color of the sole doesn't change right before you get to the blood (unfortunately) so don't let a bruise affect your judgment.

Never cut the heels lower than the widest point of the frog. As I said, I usually wind up leaving ¼ to ½ inch of heel above this point, and then I wait until the sole at the heel area starts to remove itself by flaking before I will trim any lower. The hoof will not attempt to shed heel any farther until the muscles, tendons and conditions in the hoof are ready. This is how I aim for the model without imposing it on the hoof too early. It keeps the hoof sound while also making dramatic healing progress. A lack of understanding this has been a huge wall between an army of backyard trimmers and success. I have heard people say that a freshly trimmed horse hurts "because circulation has been restored and the horse can feel the existing damage in its hooves." *This is pure rubbish.* If your trim causes pain you simply cut too deep, and you will heal nothing.

Toe

The toes of domestic horses are almost always stretched forward further than they should be away from the coffin bone. This brings the breakover point too far forward and continually pulls new growth out with it. It also pulls the heels forward and is another important factor causing under run heels. Misunderstanding that the toe is stretched forward, rather than being too high vertically, leads to the most common and serious mistake in the farrier world. This "rotated" hoof looks like a duck's foot if the horse's heels are lowered, so people will rasp away at the toe callous to lower the toe and attempt to raise the heel to "stand him up." They are rasping an area that is already too short and building up an area that is already too long in most cases and the results are a horse that is shut down without hoof protection, at best. At worst, the horse is doomed to live a short painful life stuck in a founder cycle. Rasping the sole at the toe in preparation for a shoe is precisely what causes a hoof to "need" a shoe most of the time. I used to do it, too, and it is something I deeply regret.

The sketches on the facing page show the most common domestic hoof form I have seen all over the country and misinterpretation of it is causing horses a world of trouble. The toe in the top sketch is stretched forward and this gives the appearance to an overwhelming number of farriers in the field that the toe should be lowered and the heels raised. This toe is far too *short* vertically, but is commonly mistaken for a toe that is too long.

Making Natural Hoof Care Work for You

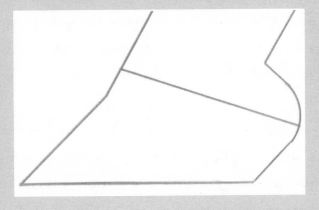

"This sketch shows the most common domestic hoof form I have seen all over the country and misinterpretation of it is causing horses a world of trouble."

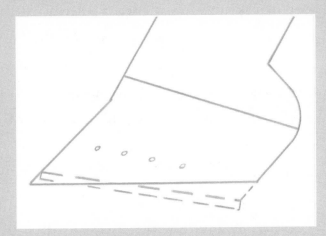

"The dashed line . . . is the exact opposite of what the hoof needs."

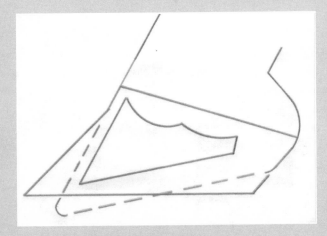

"The true hoof that the horse needs to grow is represented by the dashed line. The band of steep hoof just below the coronet shows us that the horse is trying every day to grow this hoof.

The result is represented by the dashed line in the center sketch (*facing page*). It is the exact opposite of what the hoof needs. Hopefully the error in this is already clear to you, but I am seeing it *every* day by professional farriers all over the country. The bottom sketch reveals the approximate coffin bone position. The true hoof that the horse needs to grow is represented by the dashed line. The band of steep hoof just below the coronet shows us that the horse is trying every day to grow this hoof.

All you have to do to achieve this is *allow* the horse to grow it on his own. This can never happen if you let the heels grow longer. Everything below the dashed line needs to be removed. As you can see by the sketch, the toe callous and most of the quarters are already way too short, so obviously the hoof can never reach its proper form if that area is rasped or knifed at every trimming. *If you are a farrier and you are going to only remember one point from this book, this needs to be the one!* As a general rule, leave the sole at the toe alone unless you must lower one side to balance a hoof.[†] Balance the toe by sighting across the already balanced heels from the back of the hoof as you rotate the hoof from you in the arc of its joints. The plane across the toe should be parallel to the plane across the heels and both should be perpendicular to the range of motion of the pastern and coffin joints.

Seldom will you need to lower the sole at the toe area on a horse that has

---

[†]As I write this, I have strong feelings I am teaching an incorrect method. This is the way I balance hooves and it has served the horses in my care very well, but the wild model shows us that active wear points show up in different areas of the toe. I find it very common for the inside of the front toes to build a slight "bump" and thus be an active wear area in that region while the rest of the toe remains passive. I respect the adaptation of a naturally wearing hoof enough that I know the horses would be better off if they were allowed to wear this "imbalance" (assuming they were never worked on a flat, hard surface) but pride in my work has kept me from experimenting with this outside of my own herd. It would be hard to leave a hoof that everyone would think was out of balance; right? Still, every time I rasp a bit of calloused sole at one side of a toe to "balance" it, my intuition screams at me that it is not the right thing to do. The only way I can justify "cosmetically" balancing the hoof in this manner to myself is by reasoning that a wild horse would never be on a flat, hard surface as our domestic horses often are. In the future I expect to find that horses perform better if the toes are allowed to form active wear points where they please, rather than being cosmetically balanced by humans.

been barefoot, but after pulling shoes there is often excess dead sole buildup in that area. Trim away this dead, flaking sole until you get to firm, live sole. Like at the heels, stop when the flaking sole stops. Generally after the first trim, the horse should need the toe callous left alone if he remains barefoot and under steady care.

Now we are to a point in our trimming where the horse is standing there with his heels low and the front of his sole left alone, and he looks like a duck. We have made the coffin bone ground parallel or close to it, as it should be, but now the hoof wall flares forward, rather than down toward the ground. If that long, stretched out toe is left like that the strain to the entire body will be enormous, and it will keep pulling the new hoof growth away from the coffin bone for the rest of the horse's life. We must stop that cycle. You will find this to some degree in almost every hoof you start up.

If there is a widening of the white line at the toe or if there is a dish in the toe wall when viewed from the side caused by an angle change below the coronet as discussed earlier, the toe is flared away from its optimum position and needs to be backed up (see sketch at right). This serves two purposes. First, it immediately backs up the breakover point, allowing the horse to move normally. This normal movement begins the process of allowing the horse to form his perfect hoof. Second, the lever forces that are pulling the hoof wall away from the coffin bone are eliminated so that the hoof is free to grow in with firm attachment to the coffin bone.

It is important to note that a dish or angle change in the toe wall will point to separation or toe flaring even if the white line is not widened at the ground level. The sole at the toe is often pulled forward with the flaring hoof wall, causing the white line to keep a normal appearance even in some hooves with high degrees of coffin bone rotation. In this case you will see a "wider than natural" distance from the apex of the frog to the toe wall.

Don't worry about making the horse sore by removing flared toe wall. The toe callous is intended to be a very active wear area. It supports weight very

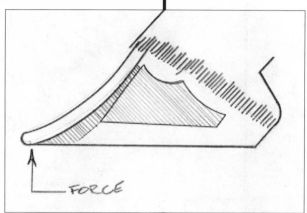

FORCE

"If there is a widening of the white line at the toe or if there is a dish in the toe wall when viewed from the side caused by an angle change below the coronet . . . the toe is flared away from its optimum position and needs to be backed up."

comfortably provided that it is not trimmed too low by a wayward trimmer. If the hoof wall is flared away at the toe (or anywhere else for that matter), it is not offering any support for the horse anyway. The horse will continue to be at a slight disadvantage until straight growth reaches the ground and you can allow the hoof wall to take the bulk of the load as nature intended. As long as the toe is stretched forward and the white line integrity is compromised, the toe will never be able to bear full pressure without continuing to tear away from the bone. We must stop this vicious cycle. Nature didn't intend for the toe to ever get stretched forward to begin with, so we are forced to do an unnatural thing for a while to correct it.

It may surprise you, but backing up the toe can be a tremendous pain reliever. If the white line is being ripped a little with every step, as it is in most of the cases we are discussing, I can only compare that in my mind with my fingernail being slowly torn from my finger. I have seen hundreds of horses, ranging from slightly "ouchy" to immobile from chronic laminitis, go completely sound just by backing up the toe to the white line and completely leaving the toe callous alone.

How much to back up the toe depends on how much damage there is and how high up the hoof it goes. Obviously if the toe growth is straight from the hairline to the ground and not stretched forward we will not back it up at all. If the white line is stretched (widened) at the toe or if there is a large angle change below the coronet, back it up to or near the white line. Gradually decrease the width of the cut as you approach each side, so that by the time you get around toward the quarters the cut will come out, so that you are cutting a crescent moon shape with the widest point being the center of the flare. (See photos in this chapter's "Basic Trim Practicum".)

If there is only slight deviation in the toe angle, or if the straight growth has almost grown all the way out and the white line is not widened, you can allow a portion of the width of the toe wall to contact the ground, but be careful not to let the toe stretch forward again.

To save time and sweat, I make this cut with the nippers. Hold the nippers so that the cut is perpendicular to the bottom of the hoof. This work can be done from the top with a rasp instead, but I like to do this initial cut from the bottom so I can see the white line and tell where I am. It is best not to do this by rasping down from the bottom of the hoof if the white line is compromised, or especially if the horse is laminitic. This action stretches on the lamina and causes pain. Try filing upward on your fingernail and you'll get the picture.

This will continue to be necessary until the new, firmly attached hoof wall has grown to the ground. At this point, of course, the toe will no longer need to be backed up and the horse can enjoy the full benefit of naturally shaped hooves for the rest of its life. The hoof wall will bear the active pressure and the deeply concaved sole will bear passive pressure as nature intended.

The Quarters

The quarters (the hoof wall lying between the heels and toe) should be allowed to hollow out, meaning that if the hoof is placed on a flat surface, the quarters will not quite reach the ground. Again, the wild model shows us that this is correct. Domestic horses show us this as well by attempting to return to this state any time they get a chance. This is very common, but again, it is not something we will force on the hoof. If this hollowing is natural for an individual hoof, it will show up as a hoof trimming guide for you in the calloused sole.

If the horse has been barefoot, this hollowing will probably be in the sole already so you can simply follow the sole with your hoof trimming. Even if the horse has been shod, when you scrape away all of the dead sole you will usually find that this shape is already present in the live sole. You *do not* trim into firm sole to achieve this hollowing of the quarters. It is so natural the hoof will do it for you. Farriers will attest to this because special care must be taken to keep from cutting the quarters too low for shoeing. This fact is further proof that this is the natural state of the hoof. Leave the hoof wall standing slightly above the sole at the quarters. Just enough to catch your fingernail on will be about right. *Never leave the quarters higher than the plane between the heel and toe. This would contract the hoof like wildfire and would be extremely unnatural.*

The thin quarters usually found on shod horses are simply caused by adaptation. The horse is attempting to resist the unnatural level trimming by producing a thin hoof wall that will wear faster. *After the horse has been under natural care the hoof wall at the quarters will be as thick as it is anywhere else.* Check out the hoof wall thickness on the Quarter Horse shown below. This picture was taken somewhere in the middle of a trim before the hoof wall was rolled. Can you honestly look at a hoof like this and even suggest nailing steel to it?

The Sole

I must stress again that all of our discussion about the trimming of the entire sole applies to the first trim of an overgrown hoof. A deep understanding of this will help you pull shoes off horses and usually have them working comfortably right away. Pay attention to these parameters as time goes by and be sure the concavity doesn't fill back in. That said, go to great lengths in everyday trimming to leave the outer inch or so of the sole alone. Any area of sole with a slick, shiny callous should keep it. Generally after the initial setup trim the outer inch of sole from bar to bar will be left alone completely to callus and we *follow the callused sole* with our trimming of the hoof wall.

After the horse has been under natural care, the hoof wall at the quarters will be as thick as it is anywhere else.

In other words, rather than trimming the hoof wall to certain standards and cutting the sole to match those standards as most of us were taught, we will instead trust the firm hardened sole of a barefoot horse to show us exactly where to trim the hoof wall. This is assuming, of course, that the horse is turned out continually, or a great majority of his time, with other horses so plenty of movement is possible.

In arid regions, the excess dead sole and frog will be like rock if the horse has been barefoot. In wet regions, the dead sole that needs to be removed is generally powdery or flaky. In arid regions, the dead sole will be slick and

Making Natural Hoof Care Work for You

polished, and distinguished from good calloused sole only by deep cracks or grooves. The same parameters apply, and this excess needs to be removed, but the labor involved in the initial setup trim is *intense*. Horses in arid regions are at an advantage, and transition to rock crushing bare hooves is easy, once this rock hard excess sole is removed. The horses seem "set free" when the hoof is first concaved. I can only compare it to you having a golf ball in your sock underneath the arch of your own foot. If steady care is maintained, it will never be so difficult to trim again, so keep your chin up. A pair of "half round" nippers will make the initial sole trimming in arid regions much easier; in wet regions, a hoof knife probably be all that is necessary.

Frog (Important updates available under "Articles" at www.hoofrehab.com)

The expansion and contraction of the entire hoof capsule is a blood pump. The frog is not. The frog is a flexible area that allows the hoof to expand and it also plays a small role in the giant shock absorbing system of the horse. It also is a traction surface to aid horses descending rocky terrain. In the natural hoof the frog extends all the way across the back of the foot. The heel bulbs and frog are one unit and it is tough and leathery. Think about the difference in traction on asphalt between a steel wheel and a rubber tire and you will see what I mean. (Hey, I could start a horseshoe discussion with that one!) Study the hooves of any other hoofed animal and you will probably agree. Even though they are cloven, the hooves of deer, cows and goats all have the same general design, with a hoof wall in front for digging traction while running forward and leathery pad in back for easing downhill on rocks. It's wonderfully versatile, and it works.

In most domestic horses the heels are so long and contracted that the only purpose the frog serves is as a bacteria trap and a soft area that can easily bruise if it is overgrown. Because it is a naturally softer material than the hoof wall, the frog grows very quickly to compensate for wear. If the heels have been left high or if a shoe is present, the frog will get very long in a hurry. Cut the frog flat (level with the ground) in a straight line from the level of the trimmed heels to the lowest point of concavity at the point of the frog (to or close to the spot where the "dirt line" at the apex would disappear. Trim away the "flaps" on the

> "The expansion and contraction of the entire hoof capsule is a blood pump. The frog is not."

sides at a 45 degree angle so that they do not harbor bacteria.

If thrush is present trim away *all* of the black, rotting material and treat the frog with your thrush remedy of choice.

A Practical Note about sharpening your hoof knife

If you can't sharpen a hoof knife so that it will shave hair, you'll want to learn how. I generally sharpen between every horse, but I am probably the pickiest person you will find anywhere. (Plus it is a chance to rest without anyone knowing it!) Most hoof knives come with a fairly steep edge. I create a long, razor edge angle with a chainsaw file. The area I am filing winds up about $^3/_{16}$ inch wide rather than the $^1/_{16}$ inch edge that comes stock on most knives. After that initial angle change I keep the edge honed with an oval diamond stone. Also use the diamond stone to remove the burr on the flat (back) side as you sharpen, being careful to hold the knife perfectly parallel with the sharpening stone. (The chainsaw file should only be used for quick reduction as the cut is too coarse to achieve razor sharpness.)

The flat, razor edge is far less durable but I want my "under the horse" time to be as efficient as possible. If you sharpen your knife this way you can use it to reduce an overgrown hoof wall with it quicker than most people can get their nippers out of their pocket. You will of course have to sharpen this long, weak edge more often. The knife companies will love me for teaching this, I'm sure. A knife lasts most farriers for all or most of their careers. I go through one every two months, but it's well worth it if you're trimming fifteen or twenty horses a day.

The same goes with all of your tools. I keep my nippers well-sharpened and the first time a rasp fails to make a pile of "coconut shavings" with every stroke I'm done with it. Whether you are a horse owner in a "life or death" struggle to trim one horse, or a professional trimming twenty horses a day, sharp, quality tools will be worth their weight in cut diamonds to you when you are out at the end of your rope.

Making Natural Hoof Care Work for You

From the Top

I tend to do a lot of rasping on the lower $^1/_3$ of the outer hoof wall for several reasons I'll explain here. A stigma against doing this, held by many farriers, has been a stumbling block for many horses (literally). This has long been a controversial topic in the farrier world, but it has served my horses well. The wild model shows us that the outer wall is supposed to be heavily abraded.

One reason I rasp the outer wall is to check any separation of the white line. We have talked at length about toe flaring already. Putting a stop to a quarter flare works much the same way. We must rasp the flare off, so that the flared hoof wall doesn't keep pulling the new growth out with it and perpetuate the problem. Again, this flared hoof wall is not helping to support the horse's weight anyway, so removing it doesn't seem to make the horse less comfortable. I generally extend the line of the upper $^2/_3$ of the hoof growth the rest of the way to the ground in a straight line all the way around the hoof by rasping any flaring away. The exception to this would be that if the flaring is so great that removing it requires rasping past the white line. In this case, stop at the white line and keep working it back at each trim. As we discussed with toe flaring already, the removal of quarter flares doesn't cause soreness as you might expect because the flared hoof wall isn't helping to support the horse anyway. The horse will continue to be at the same disadvantage, though, until the well connected growth reaches the ground and starts to do its natural job. Again, we are forced to do an unnatural thing for a while to allow the hoof to repair itself so that it can be optimum.

At the toe, do the same thing. We already established our breakover point from the bottom (see sketches at right, *top*). If we previously backed up the toe a considerable amount, there will be a squared cut left at the end of the toe. Thin the lower $^1/_3$ of the toe until the squared-cut is only about ¼ inch wide in preparation for the "mustang roll" (right, *bottom*). In other words, try to make the hoof appear normal from the top using the lines created from the bottom. If it was not necessary to back the toe up from the bottom, still remove any flaring in the lower $^1/_3$ of the hoof wall. By "flaring" I mean any

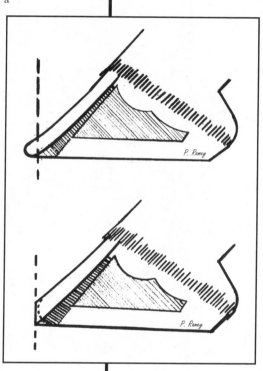

With a severely flared hoof, the work can be sped up with a vertical nipper cut (*top*). This hoof wall is too disconnected to aid in support anyway, so rendering it passive will not sore the horse and will allow well-connected hoof wall to grow in. Finish by rolling the hoof (*bottom*).

outward turn or bend in the hoof wall.

This removal of flare serves several purposes. It makes the hoof look more natural for one, and it immediately gives the horse a smooth natural breakover. By thinning an area it will wear faster, so it is less likely to grow long between trims and stretch the white line we are trying to allow the horse to repair. You can use thinning to keep the hoof at its optimum form between trims by thinning areas in a particular hoof that tend to grow out quickly. As the hoof gets healthier and the tight white line grows in, less and less of this thinning will be necessary, until finally, if living conditions, diet, and trimming are correct you will find you aren't doing it at all. This is the main point I must stress. We are "aiming" the natural upper growth (close to the coronet) straight to the ground by keeping the flared growth rasped back. When the tightly connected growth reaches the ground it will not be necessary or desirable to rasp it anymore. The horse will have no flaring and the breakover will be in its optimum position without further adjustment.

Hoof wall thinning is also a major tool for the balancing of crooked hooves. If an imbalance in a particular hoof tends to keep returning, thin the wall in the area that keeps growing too long. Again, this will cause that area to wear faster, keeping the hoof balanced. When attempting to correct an imbalance while shoeing, the imbalance always comes back by the time the shoe is reset because the hoof wall can't wear. This "back and forth" balancing perpetuates the problem. By leaving the hoof bare so that it can be kept balanced, it usually isn't long before the imbalance doesn't return.

With the hoof on the stand or knee, move your eye directly above the hoof so that you are looking straight down on it. The hoof wall should be fairly parallel to the hairline all the way around. A bump in the hoof wall from this view will give a clue about how the area should probably be thinned.

Mustang Roll

Finally, finish the entire hoof wall with a mustang roll (*left*). Study the wild hoof pictures. I use about a $^3/_8$ inch radius. It is easiest to start the radius from the bottom with the rasp and then bring the hoof forward to finish. This makes

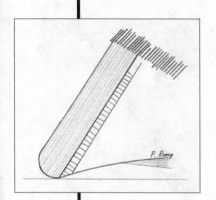

Finish the entire hoof wall with a mustang roll . . . this makes hooves look beautiful to the eye, and starts the process of callusing.

Making Natural Hoof Care Work for You

hooves look beautiful to the eye, and starts the process of callusing we discussed earlier.

If this is a first trim, there may be nail holes or broken areas of hoof wall. If so, roll the area the best you can and wait for the problems to grow out. It will also help if the horse owner is able to touch up the roll in these tattered areas between trims.

Inspection

The final step is important. Stand back and look at what you have done. The hooves should be uniform in length and well balanced. Viewed from the front, the hairline should parallel the ground and the angle of growth (grain) should be perpendicular to the ground at the toe. The hinds should be at a steeper angle than the fronts. We don't talk very much about hoof angle, because we respect whatever angle the horse is trying to produce at the coronet. Normally, though, the hinds will be at least five degrees steeper (more upright) than the fronts. If your horse didn't turn out that way, you probably missed something. Don't neglect the hinds. They can transfer many problems through the entire body and even dramatically affect the front hooves. They don't tend to get sore very often, so people have a tendency to "let them go", but a long hind toe causes most of its problems in the horse's back. Although the domestic horse is plagued with back problems, they are seldom diagnosed and almost never blamed on the hind feet. A great majority of back problems get diagnosed as training or attitude problems so take care of your hinds. They just might be causing more problems than you think.

Much has been written about the angle or straightness of the hairline when viewed from the side. To stay comfortable through rehabilitation the hooves need to be trimmed on the parameters I have given here. To try to make trimming decisions based on the angle or straightness of the hairline is a mistake. Horses in competent natural care will wind up with a hairline that (viewed from side) descends in a fairly straight line or a slight dome, almost to the ground once they are fully transitioned. This is another area where the wild model needs more scientific research.

Okay, the remainder of this chapter (*overleaf*) gives examples of the basic natural trim discussed so far.

*Overleaf: first time natural trims given to various breeds and ages of horses.

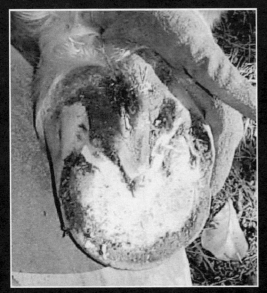

THIS QUARTER HORSE has no white line integrity in the lower half of his hoof. We must eliminate the forces pulling the hoof wall outward or this will continue to plague this horse for the rest of his days. The hoof wall is offering little or no support, since it is flared so severely that any upward force from the ground can only tear the lamina further. It seems that few people would be surprised that this horse is perfectly sound on pasture, but are shocked when we take away his flaring hoof wall, thinking that we are robbing his support. He is walking on his sole, now, and the lamina tear a little with every step. By eliminating the forces causing the separation, we take away one source of pain.

This horse could not be expected to be ridden barefoot on rough terrain, because of the lack of concavity, white line integrity, and hoof wall support, but is very comfortable being ridden in sand or grass. In three or four months his hoof will have grown the rest of the way in, and he should become very capable. This horse could be shod right now, and be ridden on rough terrain, but if that is done, he'll always be in the same boat. By continuing with steady natural hoof care, the light at the end of the tunnel is not too far away. This horse could also be ridden now in hoof boots on rough terrain and his healing would not be interrupted. Actually, the extra movement would speed his recovery.

Natural Trim
12 Year Old Quarter Horse

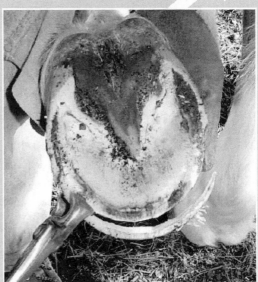

(*Left*) Severely flared and overgrown hoof. (*Right*) Removing flare vertically with the nipper saves a lot of backbreaking rasping.

1

5

The finished product should be as or more comfortable than it was before you started. This horse is ready to ride. Look for the heels to recede in time, but don't try to force them down by rasping into quality, live sole.

Always balance the heels.

2

Note the well-connected growth in the upper one-third of this hoof. We must allow this straight growth to reach the ground.

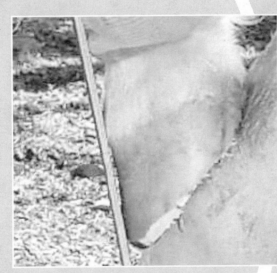

3

Allow flare to grow out by rasping the lower one-third of the hoof wall to make it match the angle of the upper two-thirds of the hoof wall, all the way around the circumference of the hoof.

4

Step 1

After rasping the hoof wall to the desired level, remove the flared hoof wall with the nipper, using the white line as a guide. Also note that in this hoof, the sole was only cut close to the frog, and at the bars. Hollowing the sole deeper at this point would lame the horse, which is of course unacceptable. This toe could actually have been backed up all the way to the inside of the white line if necessary in a more extreme case without injury to the horse. This nipper cut will be used as a guide for working the hoof from the top.

Step 4

By thinning the flared hoof wall all the way around, we cause it to wear faster…it also has the added benefit of making the hoof look good.

Step 5

Note that the calloused outer band of sole was not cut. It will be allowed to grow thicker. Trimmed this way, the quick will be driven up, and the heel can be lowered more each trim until it reaches its optimum height. If I had taken the heel down farther, the horse would have been less comfortable, and slowed healing by reducing movement. The horse is more comfortable than when we started, and his hooves are set up to get better and better every day.

75

Natural Trim
3 Year Old Tennessee Walking Horse

At the upper ½ inch of hoof wall, it is easy to see what the horse is trying to grow.

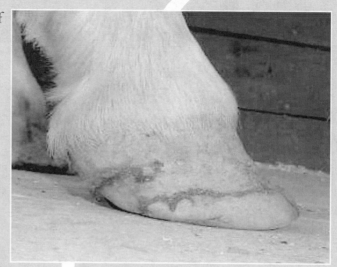

1

Trim Notes

(Step 1) This horse was lame in epoxy shoes. The owner had tried bar shoes with pads. His problem should be obvious to you by now. Everyone who touched these hooves had rasped the toe callous area, where it is too low already and tried to let the heel grow. This steadily made the poor horse worse.

(Step 2) If you keep it trimmed properly the healthy growth will grow on down, and the heels will steadily become even lower.

Making Natural Hoof Care Work for You

To fix this mess, simply
lower the heels, and back up
the toe to the white line.

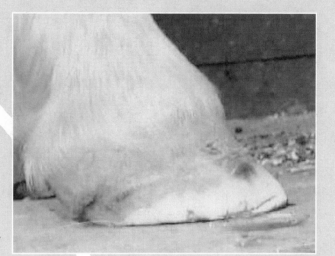

2

This horse became
comfortable immediately.

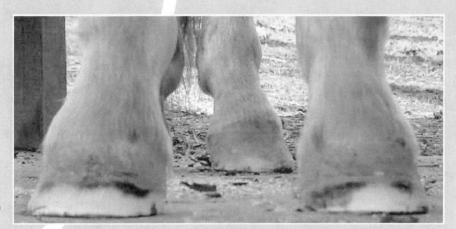

3

This hoof needs some work!

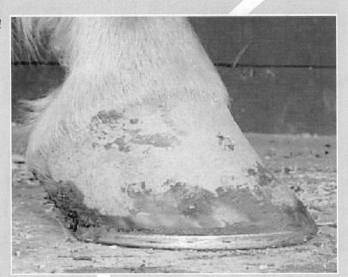

1

What a relief for
this girl, I'm sure!

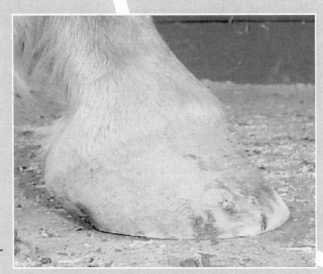

4

Clean out any chalky, dead sole and lower frog and bars appropriately.

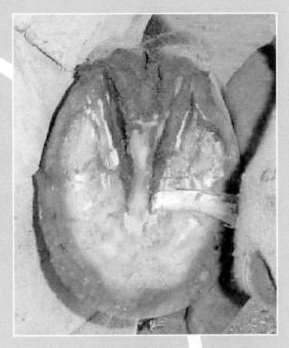

2

Using the nipper, make the hoof wall the same thickness all the way around. This will discourage future flaring. Also note that the firm sole has not been trimmed.

3

Step 1

This horse seems sound in her shoes, but is shut down when she throws one, and the long heels, stretched white line, and dishing toe spell trouble on the horizon. This horse had been shod only two weeks earlier.

Step 2

Note how quickly I reach the frog/sole juncture at the point of the frog. It was only $1/16$ in. deep. This means we will definitely be leaving this sole alone. The coffin bone is very low in the hoof capsule.

Step 3

The sole was lowered only at the heel and bar area until the loose flaky material was gone and quality live sole was reached. The rest of the sole is already too thin. This is how the frog/sole juncture is such an important guide. Without it, we may have misread this hoof as one that could be cut much shorter than this and deeply concaved. We would have had a bloody mess on our hands.

Step 3

This is the new beginning for this girl. She was comfortable immediately, but will need some time before she can carry a rider on rough terrain without boots. Her heels will de-contract, the sole will get thicker and more concaved, and the hoof will grow in straight with a tight, healthy white line.

The Basic Natural Trim

Natural Trim
10 Year Old Welsh

This was one of those really memorable, wonderful days. This pony was practically immobile in heart bars, and had been for three years.

1

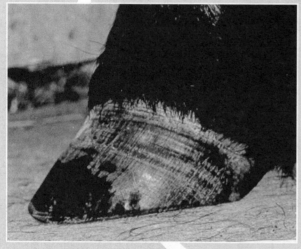

3

This was my first trim. When we turned him out, he was so excited he just ran back and forth in his paddock. He never limped a step after that day, and continues to be ridden barefoot.

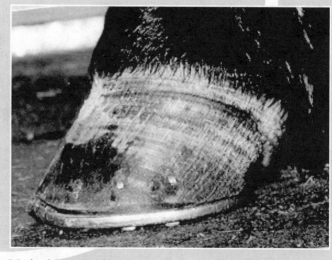

2

He had been under the very best available conventional care for the duration. This was no case of neglect. Radiographs show 14 degree rotation. A quick glance at the coronet gives the same information.

Making Natural Hoof Care Work for You

20 Year Old Mule

This is the first trim of a mule with a very tattered hoof wall from excessive length and neglect.

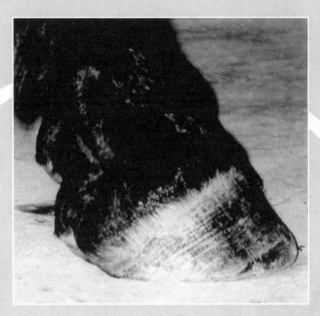

1

He proceeded to grow in a healthy strong hoof.

2

The Basic Natural Trim

The frog tends to be farther behind the heels than in horses, and the coffin bone is much smaller for a given hoof size than in a horse. The frog bears weight very well and the trimming parameters are the same. Mules and donkeys are very tough and have strong hooves. Putting shoes on them is truly a waste of effort. I have never seen or heard of a well-maintained mule or donkey being tender footed and can't imagine why anyone has ever felt the need to protect their feet. If you go in the natural hoof care business you will find that the owners of mules will flock to you in droves. You will be able to turn their "typical" short, stiff legged gaits into long smooth strides and they will love you for it. I, of course, let the individual hooves give the final answer, but I have found that most mules and donkeys with healthy feet can be maintained successfully on eight to twelve week trimming schedules.

"Our job is simple."

Natural Trim
10 Year Old Quarter Horse

This is the first trim on a very separated and flared hoof. Check out the under run heels and stretched toe. He is already barefoot and is somehow comfortable, so we will of course keep him that way while still allowing him to grow a more natural and able hoof.

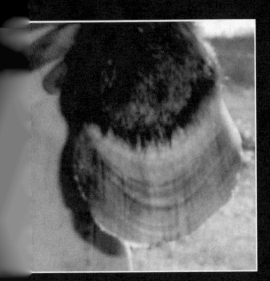

You can see the band of tight growth at the upper ½ inch of the hoof. This shows us that the horse is working to grow a healthy hoof, so our job is simple. We will just allow him to do so.

Here I have found the lowest point of concavity at the point of the frog and taken down the bars to the desired height. The available concavity is shallow, so this is it for sole cutting.

1

Finished -- view from behind.

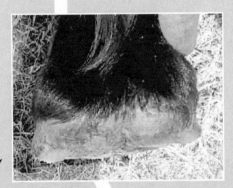

7

That's it! He is still comfortable and there is nothing left to stop him from growing a perfect hoof.

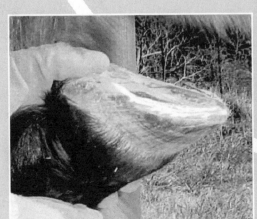

6

The excess hoof wall is removed.

2

The flared hoof wall is cut back so it will not continue to pull new growth with it.

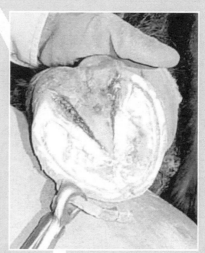

3

Flare removed.

The flares in the outer wall are thinned too so they will cause fewer problems in the future. You could skip this step, but you would have to trim again in a week, rather than in four, as I will this one.

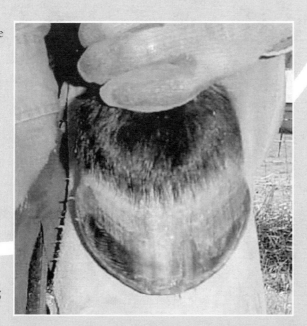

5

4

Natural Trim
15 Year Old Thoroughbred

This older race horse is well on his way to recovery from a 10 degree rotation as you can probably see in the upper inch of the hoof wall. Note that his toe is backed up to the white line. He is comfortably trail ridden barefoot in one of the roughest areas around, and I have seen him do something similar to a back handspring in the pasture. I am showing him to you because he is a bit of a contradiction. I would love to hack the rest of those heels off, but the sole at the heel area is rock hard and polished into a glossy callous. This is the indication that this is as low as I should go. He will grow the steep hoof the rest of the way in, and his heels will retreat with my help, but only if I leave his calloused sole to drive up the quick. Meanwhile, as his hooves continue to improve and become more naturally shaped, this horses already thinks he's completely healed.

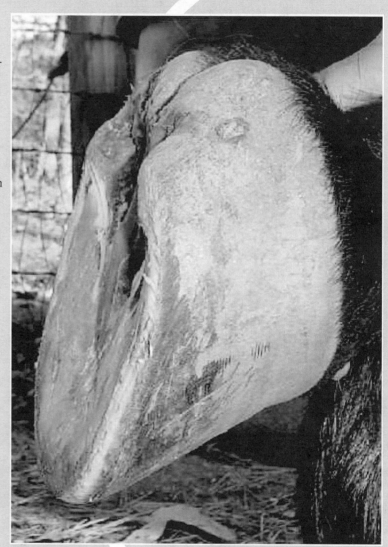

1

2

This is how we help the horse get back to the model without forcing it on him. It is the most important part of natural trimming. Not too long ago, I would have shut this horse down, in a rush to get the coffin bone ground-parallel on day one. Hundreds of founder cases taught me that I can heal this guy quicker if I respect the current conditions in his hoof and get him moving. This lesson can save you and your horses some time and unnecessary pain. Three more months down the road the heels have retreated on their own, the sole is far more concaved and he is as able and vibrant as any horse I have ever seen.

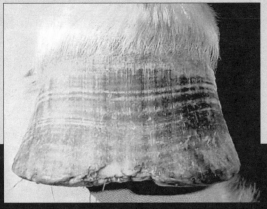

This horse has simply been neglected on pasture. There appears to be no real damage done in the upper half of the hoof.

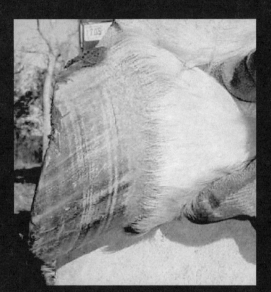

The flaring will be easy to correct.

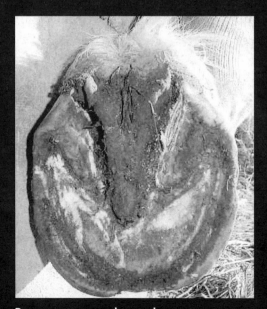

Remove any powdery sole.

Take the bars to the proper height and find the lowest point of concavity at the apex of the frog.

1

Finished product is comfortable for the horse and set up to heal.

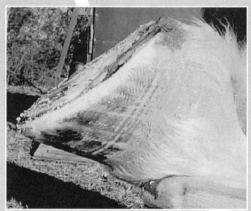

6

Remove excess hoof wall standing above the sole and balance heels.

2

Stretched white line and flared outer wall let us know that the hoof wall will be thinned so the new growth will not be pulled away from its proper attachment.

3

Flare nipped from below.

4

All flares are removed from the top.

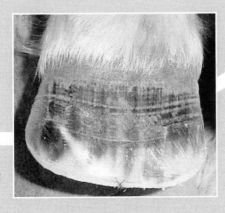

5

Natural Trim
8 Year Old Arabian
Part 1: Left Front

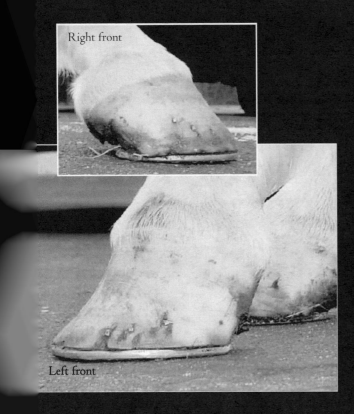

Right front

Left front

Check out these bars.

1

Only on rare occasions will you truly correct a condition that occurs on only one side with hoof care only. It is important to realize that the hoof imbalance is an attempt by the horse to adapt to an imbalance higher up, usually in the shoulder. The more you try to make the hooves match each other, the less blanced the movement will be. It is also a *big* mistake to try to make the healthier hoof match the bad one. This is what was happening to this horse. The farrier was letting the right heels grow as long as possible to try to match the left, in spite of the fact that the right heel is under-run. This horse was actually limping on the right, due to pressure from the long under-run heel. The "bad" foot was comfortable!

While it is doubtful this horse will ever be "normal", the best chance of it comes from keeping

(Continued on page 90)

88

"The more you try to make the hooves match each other, the less balanced the movement will be."

They are the
first to go . . .

Left front hoof

2

The redness (marked
by arrow) is bruising
caused by the long
bars. Don't let it
scare you away.

3

View from behind
shows shortened,
balanced heels and
mustang roll at
quarters.

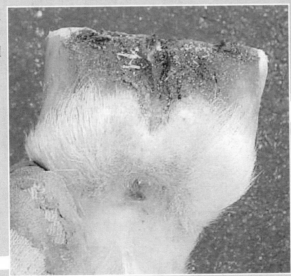

4

The Basic Natural Trim

Natural Trim
8 Year Old Arabian
Part 2: Right Front

Left front

Right front

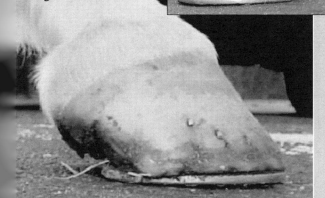

1

Finding the sole and point-of-frog junction.

(Continued from page 88)

…he right hoof healthy and normal, and …working the left hoof toward the wild …model each trim. The heels will be low-…ered as much as possible each trimming …while respecting the calloused sole. The …lished toe must be backed up so that …he new growth isn't pulled forward. …Stress 24 hour turnout with active bud-…dies.

Treat the hooves as individuals and …make no attempts to force them to …match. Above all she should be comfort-…able and ridden as much as possible.

Respecting the conditions inside the …hoof will keep you out of "tendon strain …trouble." The hoof will not show indica-…ions that the heel can be lowered past …he point the horse is ready for.

"As I said, the best we can do for this horse is get this hoof back to normal while we attempt to correct the other one."

The sole, bars, frog, heel-buttresses have been trimmed and I'm removing flare from the hoof wall.

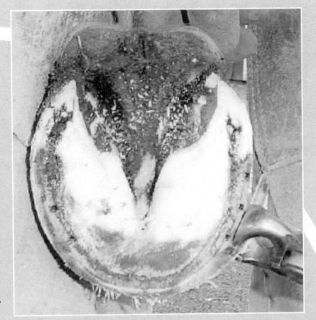

Right front hoof

This is the finished product and the horse is totally comfortable. She hasn't limped a step since that day and actually moves with surprising balance.

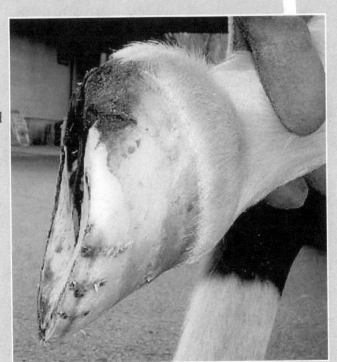

Chapter 4
Maintenance Trimming

MAINTENANCE OF FOALS

MAINTENANCE OF FULLY
    TRANSITIONED BAREFOOT HORSES

*Checking the hooves at four weeks.
"The primary factor that has led the
horse world to being convinced that the
horse must be shod is waiting until the
hoof looks damaged to trim. We must
trim before damage is done, not after. "*

Maintenance Trimming

Steady maintenance is the heart and soul of natural hoof care. You can make mistakes in trimming and still succeed, but don't make the mistake of not trimming. *The primary factor that has led the horse world to being convinced that the horse must be shod is waiting to trim until the hoof looks damaged to trim. We must trim before damage is done, not after.* As a professional, I keep my customers on a steady schedule, and they never have to think about hooves at all. If you are a horse owner trying to maintain your own hooves, I have some tips.

Trim your horses every four weeks. Set up a day of the week you will always trim, and divide your trimming. For instance: One lady I know with two horses trims two hooves every Sunday evening. (Both fronts or both hinds, of course) This way, each hoof gets trimmed every four weeks and she never forgets or has a grueling work day to dread.

I recommend that any horse owner who trail rides and wishes to maintain their own hooves buy quality hoof boots. They will make up for mistakes in your technique, get you on the trail quicker and will take the fear and anxiety out of the whole experience. You may not need them for long, but humans and waiting don't mix very well for some reason, and they will keep you from doubting yourself and from wondering if you're doing the right thing.

If you are fortunate enough to have a competent natural hoof care professional in your area, let him or her keep your horses on schedule all year. People tend to want to neglect their hooves when they aren't using them, and that is precisely what has gotten domestic hooves in the state most of them are in. Maintaining hooves year round will pay big dividends when you are ready to ride and save money in the long run by giving you extra years with your horse and reducing your vet bill. In winter, hoof production does slow down and I do lengthen the trimming periods on horses with exceptional hooves, but for

Making Natural Hoof Care Work for You

hooves that I am trying to perfect I find winter to be a great time for healing and keep the horses on their same schedule as in summer.

How do you recognize a competent professional? Your horses will absolutely love them, and they will be able to produce many satisfied customers with sound, barefoot riding horses. Everyone talks about the healing power of natural hoof care. It is easy to focus on lameness, but *what separates the good professionals from the bad professionals is soundness.* There are a lot of people out there laming horses using invasive trimming techniques and this simple test will help you weed them out.

Demand will create supply, and if horse owners in an area are begging for a natural hoof professional, you can bet someone will see a business opportunity and what to learn. I have watched this happen all over the country. I have helped several beginning professional trimmers to "replace me" in different areas in my territory. I'm not exactly hurting for more business anyway, and I truly want to see as many horses helped as possible. I beg all successful practitioners to do the same. When you see a promising trimmer who has the interest and the backbone for the work, give them a helping hand. Do it for the horses.

I have seen the trimming methods that prescribe continuous deep sole trimming, and unfortunately I have tried them. Thousands of trims have taught me to abandon such methods, and to trust the adaptive powers of the hoof. The sole of a barefoot horse will tell you precisely where to trim the hoof wall and bars if you continually remove the sole ridge around the frog and the flaky sole the horse is trying to shed. The more you try to make it complicated beyond that, the less able your horses will be. The more invasive things you do to try to un-contract heels or straighten bars or push the hoof into some "mold" the slower your progress will be, and the more uncomfortable the horse will be. Trust me, I've been there.

I have studied everything I can get my hands on about horses and their hooves, and still I can't even come close to calculating formulas for the correct heel height, toe length or angle. Simply reading the individual hoof will give it to you every time, and the truly neat thing about it is that in the end the hoof

"What separates the good professionals from the bad professionals is soundness."

will "coincidentally" agree with most of the criteria people attempt to use in hoof trimming. Most of the common contemporary ideals concerning bone alignment are correct, but it is common for people to try to push an unnatural hoof even further from nature to achieve proper skeletal alignment.

When a horse grows his natural hooves, they will be wonderfully balanced and the hoof wall will almost always be in perfect alignment with the pastern and shoulder. The heels will be almost nonexistent in length but be thick and solid and the toe will be short and have a smooth natural breakover. Contracted heels will widen and the beautiful deep solar concavity that most people think we have bred out of our horses will emerge. The horse will move the way nature intended; nimble, quick, comfortable, smooth and tireless.

Maintenance of Foals

All of the problems we have been discussing throughout this book could have been avoided. As I said earlier, the maintenance of foals is crucial. Foals are born with healthy, well-connected lamina and their hooves are ready to handle the extremes of a high desert nomadic lifestyle. By the second day of their lives they are keeping up with a herd that is moving twenty or more miles a day. The long treks to food and grazing, fleeing with the herd over rocky terrain, and hours of spirited play are all genetically coded into their tiny new hooves. They will grow rapidly to ensure that there is enough hoof wall to do the job.

Foals born in captivity are no different. Our domestic horses are born to be wild. They have the same alert, wary ways and the same sharp senses and flight instinct of a prey animal. We have learned to deal with these instincts (more or less) and managed to successfully domesticate the horse. We offer them all of the benefits of modern medicine, but we have fallen short of optimum care for these awesome creatures because we haven't bothered to study them in their natural state enough. I love to watch nature shows on TV. My favorite animal is the horse, of course, and I have read every horse book I can get my hands on, from veterinary textbooks to beginner horse care books. But I think I know

Making Natural Hoof Care Work for You

more about the lion and the crocodile than I do about horses in their natural environment. We don't even have a detailed analysis of what horses eat! Sure, we do know what *we* have fed them for generations, but no one ever bothered to study what wild horses eat before we decided what it was convenient for us to provide. This would not be quite so troubling if not for the fact that horses in the wild are not beset by most of the ailments that afflict their domestic brothers.

Most domestic horses seem to be suffering from some problem or another by the time they reach adulthood. We have really fallen short with their feet, especially. Most domestic horses' feet are so destroyed by the time they are five that they must have iron plates nailed to them so they can't feel the ground and people consider that *normal*. I'm here to tell you that it is not normal.

So far I've talked mostly about rehabilitation, but that is not my primary goal here. If natural horse care is begun before the damage occurs, there won't be anything to rehabilitate, and that is the idea that I would most like to become mainstream.

As more wild horse research is done, and compared to domestic horses, I am convinced we will find that we are seriously setting back the potential of our horses in the very first days of their life. I think we will find that the immediate leap into nomadic lifestyle that wild foals must make to be of extreme importance to development of their entire locomotion system. The breeders of performance horses will find great advantages in making the early years more natural. Wouldn't you love to see a top quality Thoroughbred raised in the wild for a few years and then brought into training?

Carefully study your foals. Anyone can easily see how quickly the hoof wall separates and begins to flare and I can only imagine the effects of the damage going on inside, and standing in the way of development. While the coffin bone shapes the hoof in later years, remember it is very much the hoof wall that shapes the coffin bone in a foal! I am holding my breath waiting for more research, but for now I'll tell you what I know.

Foals need movement. They must not be stalled and their hooves need to be competently maintained from the *beginning*. Most people start picking their hooves very young as a training exercise. With a little practice, you can trim a foal's hoof just as fast as you can pick it. The trimming guidelines are the same and they can be trimmed just like an adult, but I have found that great detail is normally not necessary with foals. What works well is much the same method I teach for beginners, which is basically a consistent removal of dead sole the hoof is trying to shed, cutting away any hoof wall standing above it and a good balancing job.

Generally, every time I trim the mother, I use only a razor sharp hoof knife and trim the excess hoof wall all the way around the foal's hooves in one continuous slice. I trim the bars and excess sole with a single circular motion as well. It takes about eight seconds per hoof, and that's it. The relative softness of the hoof and the spirited play of the foal do everything else. He just needs help with the removal of what he can't wear away because the terrain is too soft, and the travel demands are less than what he was born for.

If this sounds easy, it is. The knife method requires experience, though, and could be very dangerous in the wrong hands. A beginner should use the rasp and follow the same parameters as for an adult horse. Either way, if you keep the foal's hooves well trimmed, it will pay big dividends down the road.

Maintenance of Fully Transitioned Barefoot Horses

As hooves get healthier, the trimming should start to look a little different. Follow the same parameters, but make an attempt to avoid cutting the sole anywhere you can. It should be allowed to callous as much as possible. This does not mean we will let the hoof overgrow, only that we will respect what the hoof is telling us more than our own ideal. For instance, if you think the solar concavity needs to be only 1/8 inch deeper, or the heels ¼ inch shorter and that would mean cutting away shiny calloused sole to get there, leave it alone. Accept the fact that you are *wrong* about the hoof's need to be shorter.

The sole fills in flat in stages. First the bars get tall, and then a ridge of sole extends along the sides of the frog, and with the protection of this ridge causing the sole to receive less wear, the excessive sole begins to fill in. By trimming

Making Natural Hoof Care Work for You

the bars as discussed earlier and trimming the ridge of sole along the frog, the rest of the sole will usually maintain itself. In other words, we generally are trimming only a ¾ inch wide band of sole around the frog, from one bar, around the tip of the frog to the other bar. That will almost always be the only sole I touch on a transitioned riding horse. When this ridge is kept away the rest of the sole maintains itself more readily.

Also on a transitioned horse the thinning of the outer wall will not usually be necessary or desirable. As the flares grow out and there is tightly grown hoof wall and lamina, the mustang roll will usually be all the hoof needs from the top.

People new to natural hoof care have probably been surprised to hear of all the ways we combat excess growth. I remember when I would turn my horses out barefoot in winter and I would worry that they would break away their hooves so low I wouldn't be able to get shoes back on them. Occasionally I would "catch one just in time" and go ahead and shoe it in the pasture to be sure we still had a horse next spring. You can imagine how silly I feel about that now, but I only knew what I had been taught.

I had been taught to "leave a little extra hoof wall for a pasture trim, in case the hoof breaks away," and I had been taught to fear an unprotected hoof and sole pressure. Little did I know that if you keep the excessive growth cut back, it won't break or chip away and you will have more hoof growth than you could ever need. I compare it to our fingernails. It is not the people who work hard with their hands and trim their fingernails short who break a nail, is it? This is not simply theory; I have seen it applied thousands of times and with some of the poorest quality hooves you can imagine and have *never* yet seen a horse fail to put out sufficient growth to handle what was expected unless they were allowed to grow too long and then break. Of course, every part of every animal has its limits, but the hooves do not have to be the "weak link" as most people assume.

* * *

Okay, turn the page and check out my "Maintenance Trimming" practicum. After that, we'll move on to "Rehabilitation Trimming."

Maintenance Trimming

1100 lb. Appaloosa

Rock crushing hooves!

These are the front hooves of an 1100 pound Appaloosa at my place, ready for his four week maintenance trim. He is a very lively, capable ride and is used as a guide horse.

Our horses are ridden on rocky terrain, but are kept on a very firm, flat surface, so the bar, frog and the sole fill in quicker than pastured horses because their home environment gives little wear to these areas.

On pasture, the sole and bars actually maintain themselves better than at our place, and the underside of the hoof will "look better," but our hard surface seems to forge a slightly tougher hoof. (More on my horse keeping practices later.) It is important to keep the bars and the ridge of sole along the frog down as described in the trimming chapter, and the rest of the sole will almost maintain itself.

All of the discussions we have gone through about concaving the sole are to help you when you are faced with the first trim on a truly overgrown shod hoof. After the first trim, avoid cutting the outer inch or so of sole completely. A ridge of sole will keep popping up along the sides of the frog. Removing it each trim will allow the outer band of sole to callous and the solar concavity will get deeper and deeper.

1

There's nothing on the bottom of this hoof that isn't as tough as nails.

Trim Notes

(Step 1)

The bars are a little long here, but still acceptable.

(Step 2)

Here I have found the lowest point of concavity at the point of the frog. Note that the dirt line at the apex of the frog just disappears in a small area. I have lowered the bars and removed the ridge of sole along the sides of the frog. It is *crucial* that you note the sole that I did *not* cut. This is what maintenance trims should look like. The hoof wall only needed a slight trim at the quarters. This was done with the hoof knife. The rest of the hoof wall is standing only $1/16$ inch above hard sole, so it was left alone.

It is very important to note the hoof wall, sole, and frog that was *not* trimmed. You don't have to put your two cents worth in on every bit of the hoof. I gleefully look for spots I can leave alone.

2

Trim Notes

Step 3

This hoof imbalances itself continually at the toe at the right of this picture. It was thinned more on that side so it will stay more balanced between trims.

Step 4

As soon as I was done with this horse, his girth was tightened and he went back to work. I wouldn't think twice about climbing on him and heading across this continent, either. His hooves would be much better when we got there. He is in his second growth cycle since we got him. He was severely flared all the way around and developed tight, healthier growth, but as you can see in the upper half of the hoof wall, there is an even tighter hoof growing in. This seems to be common if you are starting out with a real mess, so don't worry about this. While you can expect dramatic improvement in the first growth cycle, the hooves will continue to improve for years.

Any flaring is removed from the top and hoof wall is given mustang roll.

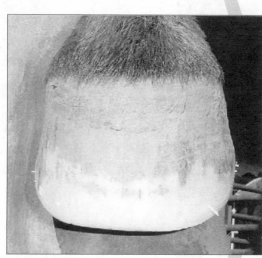

3

This is the finished product.

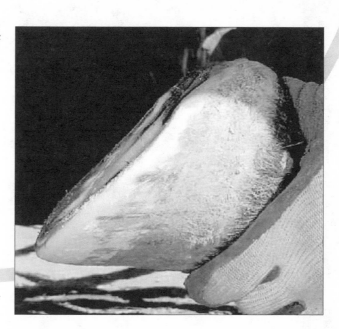

4

> "In spite of a stretched white line and flaring that are growing out, he has been sound since I pulled his shoes."

This horse has been in my care for four months. In spite of a stretched white line and flaring that are growing out, he has been sound since I pulled his shoes. The above pictures are of a front hoof before his six week maintenance trim.

Maintenance Trimming

4 Year Old Tennessee Walker

The bars trimmed and the ridge of sole along the frog is lowered to match the concavity of the rest of the sole . . .

1

He will get better and better as the new hoof wall and white line grow in, but as usual, he thinks he is already transitioned".

4

. . . and the heels
are balanced.

2

We are rewriting an
old saying: "Four
white feet and a
white nose; pull off
his shoes and watch
him go."

This is the finished product . . . the flaring has
been rasped away and the
horse is ready to ride.

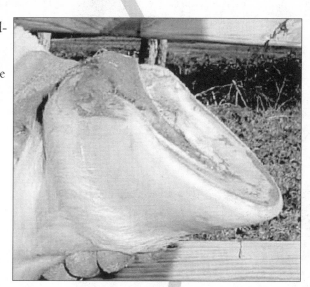

3

Ready for action, but
growing in a hoof
that is even better.

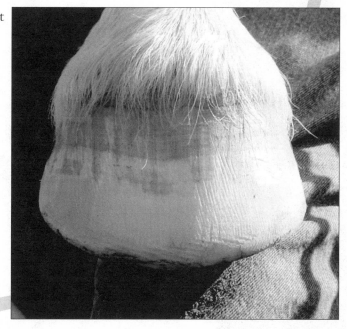

5

Maintenance Trimming

Maintenance Trimming

Quarter Horse

This is a front hoof of a very able quarter horse before his eight week maintenance trim. He is kept on pasture and ridden barefoot on rough mountain trails and gravel roads. He is ready to go anytime and can handle anything you can dish out.

If this is starting to look familiar by now, you're getting the picture.

1

Finished product.

3

Bottom of solar
dome established.

2

Finished product.

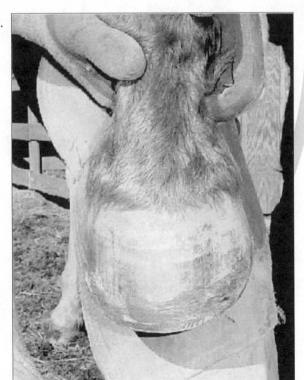

3

Maintenance Trimming

P3

P3 base parallel

Chapter 5
Rehabilitation Trimming

Rehabilitation Trimming

So far I have discussed rehabilitation in a very generic way. This is for two reasons. First, I don't know what to believe about most of what I have read and heard about the specific ailments affecting our domestic horses. Every veterinary text contradicts the next one, and almost all of the scientific research has been done on hooves that are so far from what is natural, I am forced to suspect any results.[†] So I'm sticking with what I've seen with my own eyes. I can tell you from experience that natural trimming and lifestyle changes effect dramatic results, and will work where nothing else will.

Second, most of the ailments that are plaguing our horses' hooves are caused by this unnatural hoof form. The closer you can work the hoof back to the wild model, the healthier the hoof will become. It is that simple and there is usually no need to complicate it further. A hoof professional needs to be well educated in veterinary points of view and in farrier methods, but this is mostly so that you can have an intelligent conversation with a vet, farrier, or horse owner, and describe what you are doing and answer their questions or recognize what they are trying to do and why. You can take what you learn from the wild model and totally cure a horse diagnosed with navicular syndrome, or a 20 degree coffin bone rotation, but you will have a hard time convincing the vet if you don't first study what the vet has been taught, so you can get your points across in his or her terms. Trust me; healing hooves is the easy part of this business. It is people who will make it tough.

Laminitis

We have probably already discussed everything you need to know about the

[†]Notable exceptions are Jackson's *The Natural Horse* and *HOG*, and Dr. Ric Redden's "The Wild Horse Hoof" (2001 Laminitis Symposium, see Redden's Lecture Notes)

reversal of coffin bone rotation. It is important that we realize the coffin bone is not rotating. Instead, realize that the coffin bone is in the right place at the end of the skeleton and moveable in its joints. It is the hoof that has been displaced, and all we have to do is allow new growth to surround the bone in a natural position. This will take time, and should be the least of our worries in the first days of a painful acute laminitic attack.

When a horse is suffering from an acute laminitic attack, the hoof trimming takes the back seat for a while. We must eliminate the trigger of the episode and thus, most of the pain. Move the horse to a dirt paddock, preferably with a buddy (*no stall or other forced close-confinement!*). Provide grass hay (no alfalfa or other rich grasses or legumes) and fresh water. If you plan to work on foundered horses, read "Founder" by Jaime Jackson. The first time I read it, I was disappointed by the fact that it has very little about actual hoof trimming in it. I finally realized that the detailed science and nutritional information it contains was a big missing link in my system. I was too absorbed in the hoof trimming and was having a great deal of success, but my success improved dramatically when I started paying more attention to the rest of the horse. If you only think about one piece of the puzzle, you will never get quite the success or the consistency with founder cases that is possible. In hindsight, I realize that my founder cases that have healed slower than I expected were due to my early lack of attention to nutritional details. Learn to be a stickler with the diet and the lifestyle and movement of foundered horses. Learn to get at the cause of founder.

The vet may prescribe anti-inflammatory and pain medication. I am not against this at all, as my top priority is to get the horse out of pain and moving. There will be time to grow a perfect hoof later. Reduce and then eliminate the medication as soon as possible to minimize possible side effects. I do disagree with excessive pain medication, though. As hard as it is to watch, the pain is keeping the horse from further damaging a weakened situation in the lamina. There is usually no need to be very detailed in your trimming at first. Don't put the horse through anything you don't have to. You can, however, give some very dramatic relief by relieving pressure and tearing on the lamina.

Back up the foundered toe to the white line. If the horse is miserable I get on my knees and do this work from the front with nippers so the horse will not have to stand on three feet. If the heels are high, so that the bottom of the coffin bone is not ground parallel, lower the heels. This is one of the few instances I will very carefully trim into healthy live sole. I will generally take the heels down to the widest point of the frog if the horse is foundering. This will stop any further rotation. After the acute phase (inflammation) is over, though, go back to our normal system of allowing the sole at the heel dictate heel trimming for the rest of the rehabilitation. This is important!

Don't forget the hinds. This was one of my mistakes in the past. I used to wait to trim the hinds on a horse leaning back in the founder stance, thinking that the problem was in the front feet, so why put the horse through the torture of working on the hinds. I would wait until the fronts were comfortable. When a horse has been in the founder stance (leaning back with most of the weight on the hinds) for a long period of time, the hind toes will grow long. This can force the horse to remain in the founder stance for longer than it needs to be, and makes movement more difficult. If a horse has his hinds tucked under him and the hind toes are long, I will at least back up the toe to or near the white line. I usually don't pick up the hinds if the horse is in the founder stance, but instead back up the toe with nippers with the hoof on the ground. This is especially important if the hinds are foundering as well.

On the foundered feet, keep the toe wall passive to the ground and the heels low. Trim every two or three weeks until it seems there is no excessive growth to trim that soon, and then adjust the schedule accordingly. Restrict the diet, allowing no grain. Very small amounts of assorted vegetables will make your horse just as happy to see you as a bucket of grain. As a professional, if the owners are not willing to restrict the diet for any reason, you should politely run like a scared rabbit. It is you the owners will blame if things don't go well, not the rich diet. Encourage as much movement as possible.

If rotation is really severe, the sole at the toe will be protruding or the coffin bone may be exposed. Don't let that scare you away from the heels. It is the high heel that is causing the rotation or sinking to begin with and keeping a naturally low heel is a must. You are simply following the same parameters as for a healthier, but slightly separated hoof. You are removing excess heel, leaving the toe callous alone, backing up the toe, and waiting for a new hoof to grow that is connected to the bone.

On long term neglect cases the sole at the toe may be stretched forward in front of the frog, while the white line appears to be stretched very little. You will sometimes need to back the toe up *inside* of the white line to allow normal movement and rehabilitation. I don't do this unless I absolutely must in order to achieve a normal relationship between the hoof capsule and the coffin bone. If I decide it is necessary, I make a crescent moon shaped cut with nippers around the toe perpendicular to the ground plane. I back it up enough to make the proportion of the frog/toe relationship appear typical of a healthy hoof. The distance from the apex of the frog to the breakover should roughly be half the length of the frog. I generally avoid doing this, because it just doesn't feel right, but when it is necessary it does help, and I have never seen a drop of blood from this. The live corium is back there tightly surrounding the coffin bone like it is supposed to be, so *if* you have read the situation correctly this is actually not a very invasive thing to do. Again, it is an extreme measure for an extreme situation.

Now, turn the page and let's look at several real live cases of founder and how natural trimming can work for you in the treatment of laminitis.

(Continued on page 116)

Overleaf:
Two founder
case studies.

"At some point the hooves basically gave up"

This poor mare was a truly pitiful sight. Her owner had provided her with the best available care but nothing seemed to help, so at some point they basically gave up. She had been lame for three years and her stretched toes had hurt so bad for so long, she had literally learned to graze in reverse! She leaned far back in the founder stance eating the lush grass that was killing her and would drag both front feet backward and then back up her hinds a bit to shuffle herself backward to reach the next mouthful. This is honestly how she got around!

These are her front hooves (*above*). Both front and one hind coffin bone were exposed. Now I'm a pretty optimistic type, but I wasn't making any promises. It looked pretty rough to me but I was determined to give it my best shot.

Rehab Trim
Foundered mare

She could not pick up her feet to be trimmed so I cut away all of the flaring I could from the top.

1

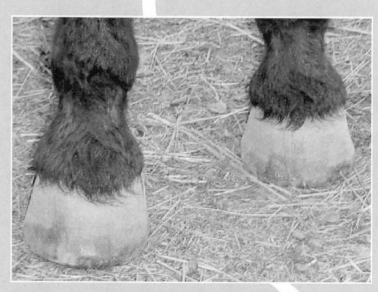

5

A slight improvement, I would say!

This was "plan B." I made a sling for her out of an old conveyor belt, hung a pulley from a tree limb and lifted her weight off her feet with the winch on my truck.

2

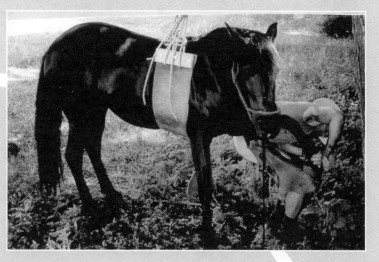

Step 1

We then put her in a corral with a buddy and hay and water. We then waited for a week, hoping she would improve but nothing changed. She continued to shuffle backward to the hay piles we scattered around and the pitiful trails she left in the dirt were sobering.

Step 2

The winch enabled me to lower her heels and the payoff was huge. She was immediately much more comfortable. She improved steadily every day until finally after two months she was completely sound on easy footing. She still had a lot of hoof growing to do, but she didn't know it. She thought she was completely healed.

Eight months later, sound and lively.

3

Step 3

The day we hung her in the sling I had vowed that I would ride that horse...and eight months later I found myself fulfilling that promise on a totally sound, wild mare that hadn't been ridden in five years. She was a handful for sure and I loved every minute of it. This is truly the most satisfying line of work I could ever imagine.

Steps 4 & 5

Here are her new hooves. There is still room for improvement as time goes by, but all of her serious problems are behind her.

Once again, she is the ruler of her beautiful valley.

4

Rehabilitation Trimming

Rehab Trim
Foundered Paso Fino Gelding

Dead lame in
reverse shoes
and pads

1

Ready to ride!

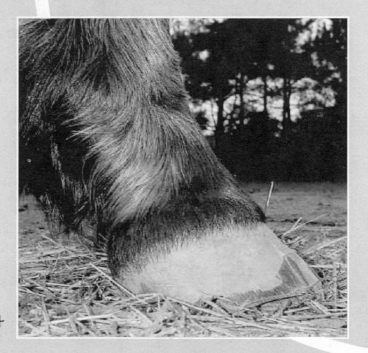

4

Entire foot, including sole is stretched forward.

2

Improving . . .

3

Step 1

This and the following pictures are of a Paso Fino that had been dead lame for three years. He had been through heart bars, wedge pads, several clinics and finally the reverse shoes and pads below, which I pulled off. Nothing seemed to give any relief.

Step 2

I found him with the tip of his coffin bone sitting almost a full inch below the hoof wall! He was immobile in shoes and pads but improved dramatically with the first trim. His comfort level went up and down for a month and then he got totally comfortable on soft footing.

Step 3

The same hoof eight months later with the horse *totally* sound on firm, gravelly ground.

Steps 4

The straight growth which is firmly attached to the coffin bone is just making it to the ground. I am still backing up the toe to the white line and will continue to do so until the very last of the rotated hoof is gone, which can take up to one cycle of new growth (about 9 months) or more. After that, the concavity of the sole will get continually deeper as the hoof grows and the sole callous drives the coffin bone higher in the hoof capsule. Even though I am continually driving toward the wild model, the horse thinks he has been healed for months.

(Continued from page III)

Navicular Syndrome

If you want to get really dizzy, read up on navicular syndrome in a few vet texts and farrier books. You will find words like "can be, often is, sometimes, occasionally, and maybe" in every single sentence. It is no wonder you can't find two experts to agree. I don't know what to believe about the exact science behind the "mysterious" heel pain, myself, but I can tell you not to nerve or put down your "navicular horse." Making them sound is almost always pretty easy.

This is my personal opinion: The deterioration of the navicular bone is caused by the body's response to unnatural pressure in that area. When heels get long and under run, the weight bearing area of the heels is moved forward, directly under the navicular bone, rather than behind it as nature intended. This puts active pressure in an area that was never intended to bear it. Also, allowing the bars to grow to the level of the heels places unnatural pressure to that region as does heel contraction. The body's defense in this case is to attempt to remove the bone just as it would in any joint with unnatural pressure being applied to it. The pain is not caused by the bone loss, but by the *cause* of this bone loss.

Like with founder, the generally prescribed treatments are the precise opposite of what it really takes to heal the horse. Simply start a natural hoof program and you will see. I have seen hopeless navicular cases go sound at the first trimming and never limp another step, or it can take a while. *It is a simple fact that I have never seen a "navicular horse" fail to be completely healed under my care.* (Oh, I'm sure that time will come, but I'm still waiting.) The body may or may not rebuild the navicular bone changes. I've never known of anyone doing an x-ray of the hoof once the horse was sound, although this would be another interesting study.

> "It is a simple fact that I have never seen a "navicular horse" fail to be completely healed under my care."

Making Natural Hoof Care Work for You

Splits, Chips, Chunks, and Tatters

By now, you already know this one. When hooves get too long the horse tries to adapt to the lack of wear. He does this by slowing hoof production, and producing thinner and weaker hoof wall. Most people aren't used to thinking of horse hooves this way, so think of a whitetail deer.

Their hooves grow and wear constantly, just like horses' and they adapt to different situations the same way. I've seen a lame deer carrying a front leg with a ten inch hoof wall and I've had to trim an orphaned fawn's hooves. The small pen it was in didn't allow enough wear for the fawn's hooves to adapt. Whitetail deer thrive in swampland, desert, rocky country and snow. Their hooves can produce the right amount of hoof wall to adapt to a wide range of habitats but if they are confined to a small pen, this is usually beyond their hooves' adaptive ability and they will grow long pointed toes.

That's exactly the situation our horses are in when their hooves are weak, brittle and breaking away in chunks. The lifestyle we have set up for them is just too easy and they are simply attempting to adapt by producing a hoof that can be easily worn away. What we are trying to accomplish with our trimming is the simulation of natural wear on harsher terrain than the horse actually lives on. When natural trimming is begun, the new growth will be beautiful. Slick, shiny horn will grow in and if the old hoof was brittle, the visible line between the two as the hoof grows out will be astonishing.

Learn to judge hooves from the hairline down. The hoof wall touching the ground is only a view into the past. A wall crack is *never* the problem, but is a *symptom* of a problem. Most cracks form after a neglected hoof flares out, or a dead, stretched white line robs the hoof wall of support. Simply fix those problems using the methods I've described here and the crack will grow out.

Wall cracks and any white line separation can often be complicated by bacterial or fungal invasion in the white line or between layers of hoof wall itself. Sometimes this black destruction will travel upward faster than we can grow hoof down. Remove any of it that you can, and soak the hooves in fifty percent apple cider vinegar and water. I recommend two hour soaks twice a

> "A wall crack is *never* the problem, but is a *symptom* of a problem."

week. Soaking boots make this easy. Other than that, I am against soaking "dry" feet. Hooves are supposed to be dry and lack of moisture is not the problem when hooves are brittle and splitting (*left*). In fact, the opposite is the case. Bacterial and fungus thrive in wet conditions. Almost always, when people are thinking a horse has excessively dry feet, the brittleness is being caused by a "too wet" environment.

Heel Contraction

Heel contraction is not so easy to identify as some people have been led to believe. A perfect, healthy heel is easy to describe and to spot. The frog will be as wide as the heel bulbs and none of the hoof wall of the heels will invade the frog's space.

What complicates the judging of heel contraction is that many domestic coffin bones have been deformed. The coffin bone doesn't stop growing until the horse is around five years old. If the heels become contracted, or if the horse is regularly shod before that time, the coffin bone actually takes on the distorted shape of the elongated hoof capsule. It is common to have elongated coffin bones and thus a hoof capsule that can never be fully uncontracted. The good news is that these horses do very well as long as no one is aggressively trying to un-contract them.

I almost left this section out completely, but decided I had to address it. Contracted heels are a big problem for the domestic horse. Contraction robs the horse of its natural blood pumping, shock absorbing expansion almost as bad as a nailed on metal horseshoe. The reason I started not to bring it up is that some people in the barefoot and farrier worlds are worrying about it *too* much. No aggressive de-contracting methods have a place in natural hoof care if they cause pain and reduce the movement of the horse. I have found that any "de-contracting" method that causes soreness in the heels makes un-contraction impossible because the horse will not bear weight on the painful heel and the heels contract more.

The very best thing I have found to do for contraction is not to worry

(*Top*) Effects of exposure to excess moisture. (*Center*) Same hoof in healing transition after given natural hoof care and dry living conditions. (*Below*) Hoof healed and free of splits.

Making Natural Hoof Care Work for You

about it. The hoof "knows" what its optimum shape is and is constantly trying to go there. All we really have to do is remove the excessive hoof that is working against the horse and allow plenty of movement on bare feet. Follow the parameters I have given in the trimming sections and the heels will de-contract if and when they are ready. Meanwhile the horse will be sound while you wait.

If contraction was present, the heels will widen. I have seen heels de-contract a full inch in six weeks, but I have also kept horses under natural care for years with very little de-contracting. In either case, if the horse is sound on his bare feet you are doing an exceptional job with his hoof care, so find something else to worry about.

Shedding Soles

If you deal with sick hooves you are going to run across shedding soles occasionally. This is just another attempt by the horse to remove what is dead or excessive. Generally there will be a healthy sole growing underneath with a foul, black layer in between the old and new. Ignore it when you trim and follow the normal parameters. It usually wouldn't cause problems to go ahead and remove dead and disconnected sole, but it is always safer to not remove sole from areas we want to build up, regardless of quality. Most commonly, you will cut through the shedding sole while making the heels correct, but there will still be some left in the toe. It will soon fall out, but let it stay as long as it will.

Abscessing

An abscess can be disheartening in the middle of a founder rehabilitation. Right when everything is going perfect and the horse hasn't limped a step in weeks, the horse can suddenly turn up miserably lame. Dead tissue inside the hoof capsule is the cause and if infection builds pressure the pain can bring a horse to its knees. To my knowledge there is not much a trimmer can do to help or prevent it. The dead tissue is already in there and the infection has to work its way out, usually at the coronet. I am against opening them unless it happens in a normal trim. The practice of finding them with hoof testers and digging deep for them does give instant relief, but can introduce bacteria to the bloodstream and set up secondary infections. I feel that it is better for the horse to let nature take its course, even though it is hard to watch a horse in pain and do nothing.

If a deep abscess is to be opened it is veterinary work anyway, and should definitely not be performed by farriers or barefoot trimmers. I would personally hate to have to explain in court why I killed a horse by performing a surgery in unsterile conditions. I have seen the vinegar soaks described earlier bring relief, but for the most part it is a waiting game. I find that this will happen at some point in about one out of ten founder rehabilitations, so it is a good idea to warn clients of the possibility.

Reality Check!

When I first started out as a professional, I was on top of the world. I had fixed all of the hoof problems at our place. We were buying every foundered or navicular horse we could find, and watching them heal. I became convinced I could fix *anything* in the time it takes to grow a new hoof capsule and there was no one to around to stand up and tell me otherwise. Sometimes it is not so simple, and I got really humbled a few times. Here is fair warning: if you get in the habit of trying to pull "incurable" horses from the edge of the grave you will find a rewarding life, for sure, but you will also get your heart broken every once in a while. This is all a part of learning, I guess. I am going to do you the service of telling you that you cannot fix them all. I am still trying to improve my ability to predict the outcome of hard cases. Any failure I see, I try to figure out *why*.

I'll give you some clues that will help you predict which cases will give you trouble. The biggest red flag should be general health. It is very common for chronic hoof problems to be accompanied by malnutrition. You will wind up banging your head against the wall attempting to rehabilitate the hooves of emaciated horses. Progress will be extremely slow until the whole horse gets healthier. On the other side of the coin, if you are trying to heal a founder and the owners refuse to quit the sweet treats and rich feed, progress will be slow or nonexistent. Obesity can make rehabilitation impossible.

Watch for hidden problems, like neighbors dumping treats to the horse. One particularly stubborn founder baffled me for eight months. He would improve, and then go back down hill, and he continued to put out laminitic growth. It turned out that there were wild cherry trees up in the woods above the barn and the horse was addicted to the bark. He had been gorging on it for years. Boy, did I feel stupid. I should have checked the whole setup at the first sign of trouble with rehabilitation (or actually before). Long term, drastically deformed founder cases can usually be immediately put on the right track by natural hoof care, but sometimes, no matter what you do, you'll get nowhere. A case in point would be complications do to club foot, where the problem probably did not originate in the hoof to begin with.

Look at the growth rings in the hoof from the side. Are the heels growing at the same rate as the toe? If so, the horse is well on his way to recovery, but I have seen the fan shaped lines continue to grow in spite of every effort. This means the heel is still growing faster than the toe and it will continue to deform the hoof capsule by creating a torque in the hoof wall at the toe, up and away from the coffin bone. I have searched for the reasons why this continues, but can't find a word about it. This pattern is started because the strain on the stretching toe lamina causes pain, which makes the horse lean back on his heels to find comfort. The added pressure on the heels encourages faster heel growth. At the same time the hoof needs relief from the long, stretched out toe so the hoof production at the toe is slowed down. What I don't understand is how sometimes this growth pattern lasts beyond the pain and inflammation. I have seen three cases in which this happened. They had each been very long term neglected cases and each of them had been malnourished. Perhaps after years of being stuck in this pattern the coronet simply "gets in the habit of it somehow." I would love to see research on this.

When you are faced with a truly deformed hoof, give it your best shot. You will probably be the horse's only hope. Be supportive, but don't be so optimistic that the owners will expect the horse to be normal in eight months. It doesn't always work that way.

I included this horse to show a little victory and a little defeat (*facing page, top*). I saw this guy in a sand lot on a back road and wound up taking him home. (I actually had to pay $300 for him, but hey, I was on a mission.) He had been this way for at least ten years. As you can see in the pictures, his toe is not growing at near the rate of the heels, and this causes a continuing curling of the hoof wall at the toe (*facing page, center*).

I want to show here that the live corium (quick) stays where it belongs surrounding the coffin bone even if the hoof is extremely deformed. If you can use the clues we have discussed to visualize the coffin bone, it will help you to "find the foot" when you are faced with something like this. I lowered the heels, which meant cutting away the eight inch bars, then cut the toe off with a handsaw. The final picture was taken twenty minutes after the ones on the facing page, and there was not a single drop of blood (*facing page, bottom*). Also, the horse went immediately from dead lame and immobile to fairly comfortable. I think there is much to be learned here.

There is also much to be learned from the rest of the story. The coronet at the toe continued to put out no hoof wall at all for thirteen months before the toe started growing. It is growing now, but still very slowly and of poor quality. The faster growing heels continue to try to twist the hoof upward. I feel that the trimming and the care have been correct, but a deformity that has been around for ten years is not going to give up easily. This is what keeps me searching for more information every day. I know that there are answers to this problem out there somewhere. I haven't given up on this guy yet, and he hasn't given up on me. He is happy and fairly comfortable but I doubt he will ever grow a normal hoof or be completely sound. I'll keep trying for the rest of his life, and hopefully learn every day.

I could have left this story out and painted you a perfect picture of a system that always leads to success, but if I gave you the idea that you could fix every hoof, I would be doing you an injustice. This is something I had to figure out on my own, and I hope to spare you some of the disappointment.

I included this horse to show a little victory and a little defeat. I saw this guy in a sand lot on a back road and wound up taking him home . . . he had been this way for at least ten years.

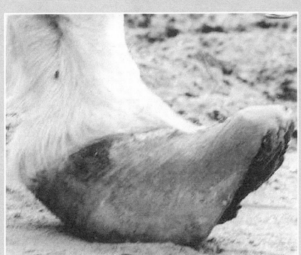

As you can see in the pictures, his toe is not growing at near the rate of the heels, and this causes a continuing curling of the hoof wall at the toe.

This picture was taken twenty minutes after the ones above and there was not a single drop of blood . . . the horse went immediately from dead lame and immobile to fairly comfortable. I think there is much to be learned here.

Chapter 6
Natural Horsekeeping

SMOKEY MOUNTAIN STABLES

Natural Horsekeeping

Barefoot horses happily cantering down a gravel road in Georgia. yours can do it too!

When I first started into natural hoof care, I set up an environment that was as natural as my available space allowed. I considered this environment to be critical to my success with barefoot horses.

When I became a professional, I found myself faced with stalled horses, pastured horses, and horses living in muck. This is the real world. What I found was that natural hoof care can work very well for horses in less than ideal conditions, but an owner should strive to give the horse all of the possible advantages. I always point out potential problems I see with new clients' horse keeping and occasionally nag old clients as well, but the truth is most people are slow to change their ways. In spite of this, steady competent hoof care can make a horse who lives in a soft, wet pasture able to perform very well, even to the point of being comfortable all day in rough terrain with a rider. A hoof on pasture under natural care is beautiful. The constant sole pressure helps to drive the solar dome upward and this gives the hooves a prettier look with healthier frogs and deeper concavity.

Still, I have never been able to get quite the gravel crunching toughness, or rehabilitate a hoof problem quite as quickly as I can at the riding facility where it all began for me, so I will include a description of this setup. This was a facility which rented horses for trail rides. I do not consider it to be a precise ideal, it is actually a very humble place, but it does produce more capable horses than any I've seen or heard of, so it is obviously worth imitating to some degree. The horses are happy, healthy, sound, and have a genuine love for life and humans. Every "horse person" who goes there compliments their condition and attitude, and there is no higher compliment for any of us, especially because almost every horse there is a hoof-related rehab

Making Natural Hoof Care Work for You

case and/or as old as dirt.

There are 24 geldings and one stud living in a 2 1/2 acre paddock. This is not exactly natural, but it works better than anything I've seen. The horses sometimes go a year at a stretch without injury, and the owners have never had a serious injury with this system. The disadvantage I see is that they have had to painstakingly take their time in introducing new horses to the herd and did have to get rid of one particularly mean varmint. Also, I do not think these close quarters would work quite so well if you added mares to the equation. You would surely need more land or fewer horses.

The horses eat free choice mixed grass hay from six round roll feeders and less than a quart of whole oats per day each. They have a salt block and mineral blocks, and are turned onto the weedy mountain pasture every once in a while as a treat. They water in the small creek that runs through a corner of the paddock, and it is dammed up in the summer so they can roll in the water. As "low tech" as this sounds, the biggest problems around there are obesity and the fact that the horses are really too spirited and lively to be "nose to tail hack horses." During the busy seasons, the horses will average around twenty-four miles a day of riding. The trail ride is steep and rocky, and they canter and jump on almost every ride and those horses love it. Every one of them is slick, shiny, and a vision of health. It is a far cry from the dull, lifeless creatures you often see at trail riding facilities.

The horses have tamped the dirt in the paddock into a concrete-like surface and the manure is scraped away with a tractor on a daily basis. There is never any muck for them to wade in. This is the most important part. This little setup would be a disaster if not for the routine manure management. It usually takes about an hour a day to feed, put out hay, and scrape the corral. Not bad, I think, considering the number of horses.

With their hooves always on this firm, dry surface, they get rock-hard very quickly, and contrary to what you may think, fatigue and soreness at work is almost never a factor. Firm ground is far more natural for horses than soft and they simply do better on it. The whole setup seems to breathe life back into "old washed up" horses, and rehabilitates founder, navicular, and wall cracks in half the time of pastured horses.

None of this is as much of an issue in arid parts of the country. I have set up eighty or so Quarter Horses in New Mexico, and it is so easy to make a perfect barefoot horse out there. The dry climate quickly tempers the hoof into the rock hard masterpiece it was intended to be. In wet regions, like my home in northeast Georgia, it is a fact that we have some disadvantages to deal with because we live so far out of natural horse country. But our type of horsekeeping setup seems to be second best only to buying a couple thousand acres in Nevada.

By now you have probably figured out I am not a big fan of moist horse feet. I'll admit I'd rather trim a soft mushy hoof; it's easier, but this was not nature's plan. The hoof should be dry and as tough as nails. Cracks, chips, and poor hoof quality are all caused by imbalance, excessive hoof length or bacterial/fungal invasion, not by dryness and almost never by vitamin or mineral deficiency.

Many times I have seen horses that were prescribed all sorts of hoof supplements for brittle, splitting front hooves, only to notice that the hind hooves had a slick, healthy hoof wall. How could a nutritional deficiency affect only two of his hooves? The same horse can go on a natural program, and a healthy hoof will immediately begin to grow.

Smokey Mountain Stables

The following pictures (*facing page, overleaf*) are of the horses at the Rocky Mountain Riding Stables where I did my first experiments with natural hoof care. The hooves look different than horses I trim that live on pasture. Even though they put in a lot of miles on rocky trails, they live on the firm flat surface of the corrals, and their hooves seem to have a little less concavity than horses that spend most of their lives on deeper footing. I need to point this out to ensure that no one is hacking into the sole of horses like this, because they are each lively, sound, and capable of working on the rocky mountain trails for days on end without difficulty.

Making Natural Hoof Care Work for You

I also intentionally included some "less than perfect" examples, so you will realize that we don't have to rehabilitate every single problem before we can succeed at barefoot riding. If you properly maintain the sole, your horses can be happily barefoot long before you "iron out" all of the problems. I could have included only perfect ideals, and tried to impress the world with their beauty, but this book is about teaching and I refuse to give half of the story. It would only be an injustice to those who are trying to help their own horses. Each of these horses is capable of doing what most people say can't be done.

The photos on the following pages (*overleaf*, "Hooves of the Rocky Mountain Stables") are all of front hooves and were all taken three weeks after and one week before the horses' maintenance trim. Each of them is completely sound and ridden barefoot almost daily on rocky terrain in complete comfort.

Go ahead and study these and I'll meet you in the next chapter, "Transition."

Overleaf: Hooves of the Rocky Mountain Stables

Hooves of the
Rocky Mountain Stables

17 Year Old Paso Fino

This guy came to the stables two years ago. He had been shod for most of his life with very high heels and was severely contracted. He may have a bit of contraction left, but he was sound and able to be comfortably ridden barefoot on day one and has been raring to go each and every day since. His gaits are wonderful and he has a spring in his step that defies his age.

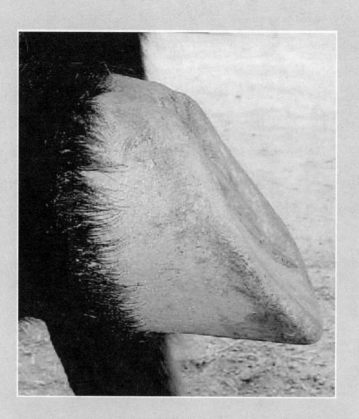

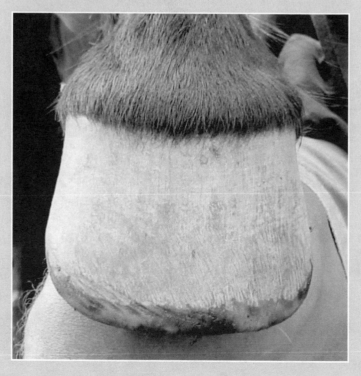

Making Natural Hoof Care Work for You

22 Year Old Quarter Horse

This horse was added to the string last year. He had a very low coffin bone position, and severe contraction. When I pulled his shoes he was a little tender at first. He was not lame by any means, but wasn't ready to ride without hoof boots. I booted him and he went right to work. Within a month he was tearing up our trails barefoot, in total comfort. He was purchased from a friend as an old "broke down" kid's horse. Natural horsekeeping and barefootedness woke him up. They have to use him for intermediate riders, because he runs too fast and is too eager for most kids. Maybe in fifteen years or so he will be back to being a plug.

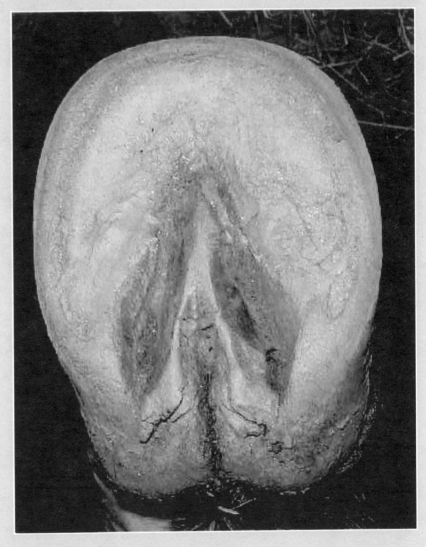

Hooves of the Rocky Mountain Stables

12 Year Old Percheron

This bruiser weighs around 2000 pounds, and is one of the liveliest rides on the mountain (*right and facing page*). The stable bought him right after they decided to go barefoot and got a real bargain, because every hoof had several splits to the hairline. As with most draft horses he was pretty sound, even with his hoof wall severely flared all the way around, and they were able to put him right to work in comfort. When the new hoof wall grew in he was magnificent. His hooves don't look perfect, but they are unbelievably tough. To watch those giant hooves slam through rocks is inspirational.

Making Natural Hoof Care Work for You

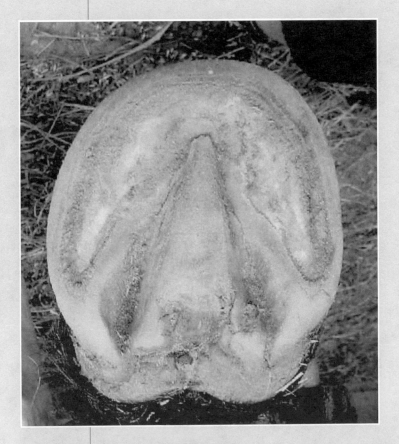

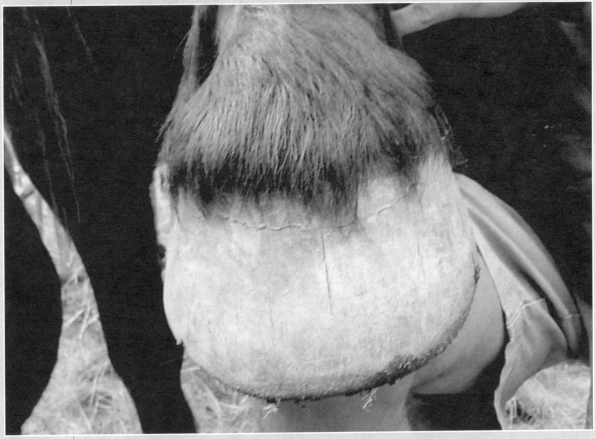

Hooves of the Rocky Mountain Stables

14 Year Old Gelding

This is one of the horses that taught me the most. As I said, I thought about using only the most perfect hooves I could find, but the best education in this book lies right here and it would have been sinful to leave it out. He's been at the stables for six years, which means he was one of the horses I used to shoe. He had heels that were an *inch apart* when he arrived, and he had obviously been foundered and had heels as long as his toes. You should have seen some of the teardrop shaped shoes I bent for this horse. He was sound in his shoes, and was a great horse. He was of course, one of the big problems I had when we first went barefoot. He wasn't miserable, mind you, but not able to be ridden on that rugged, rocky mountain. In a month his feet had

(Continued on page 135)

Making Natural Hoof Care Work for You

(Continued from page 134)

toughened up enough to be ridden on one (one hour) trail ride per day but if you tried a second ride he would get sore. At the time, I was aggressively hacking those high heels off and trying to force him to de-contract, thinking that was the problem.

While most of my barefoot horses were doing great, this horse got sore when I trimmed him. He would almost get over it, and then it would be time to trim again. Finally, after a few months I had decided that while obviously some horses could go barefoot, some could not. I had almost given up and actually planned to go back to shoeing him. I started leaving those heels alone because I was sick of making him sore, and suddenly he was sound. To make a long story short, I started learning to work with what I had, rather than trying to *force* hooves toward the wild model, and it paid off. He soon got as sound as any horse I have ever seen.

I despise his feet. I still back up his toe almost to the white line every trim. His heels have gotten much lower over time, but they still look an inch too long to me. They have also de-contracted considerably but are a long way from "correct," and I always have thrush to battle. But he is totally *sound*. Maybe I'll get him where I want him someday. Maybe I won't. The good news is that he will be in total comfort and working for a living while I wait. *He's* not worried about his feet, that's for sure.

These days, I respect the sole callous over everything else, and the payoff is in total horse comfort. The best news is that this is actually also the quickest way to fix problems as well. Often a horse like this goes through dramatic changes very quickly after natural care is begun. As I pointed out in the trimming chapter, if you hack into a long heel and invade the live sole, it registers as a wound or as excessive wear to the horse and it will spring back quickly. Conservative, competent care will always be quicker and more comfortable in the end.

Note: A few months after I took these pictures, his hooves finally decided it was time for change. He started forming powdery sole at the heels and they widened and started allowing me to lower them. Patience won and he has remained totally sound through the process. I now think he will soon have a nice looking hoof. — Pete

14 Year Old Belgian

These are the hooves of a pokey old draft horse they put people on who are scared to death. I have been doing battle with flares and long term imbalance on this guy from the beginning. Like the rest, his feet are totally comfortable and he has no idea I am trying to correct anything. That is the way it should be.

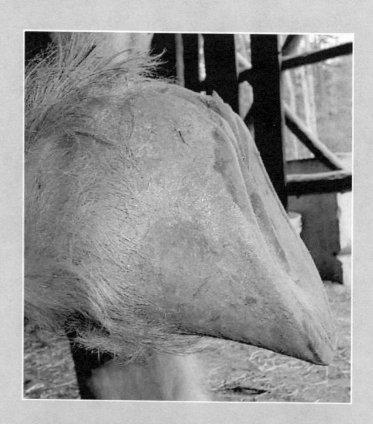

Making Natural Hoof Care Work for You

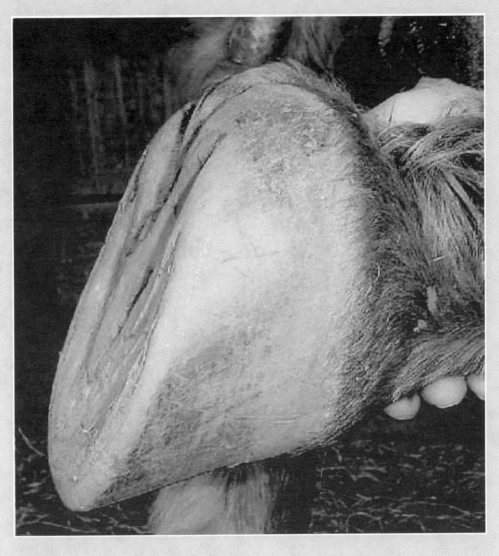

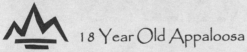 18 Year Old Appaloosa

I really like this one. I pulled his shoes a year ago. He had high heels, but they were ready to come right off without invading live sole. He never had any trouble at all.

Hooves of the Rocky Mountain Stables

14 Year Old Tennessee Walker

This is one smooth-riding, gravel-crunching high performance barefoot horse! His gaits are magnificent. You have not experienced a smooth gait until you ride a walking horse with feet like this, and that is a promise. He has been sound and on the program since the beginning. He is the foreman's guide horse, which means he probably goes three times as many miles as any of the rest of the horses.

Making Natural Hoof Care Work for You

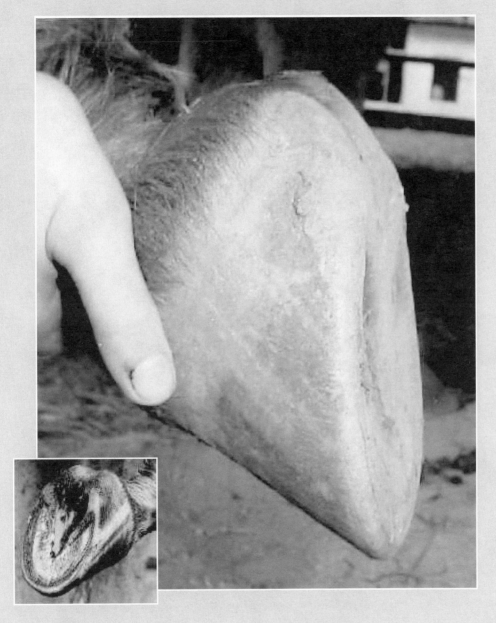

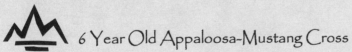 6 Year Old Appaloosa-Mustang Cross

Tough, sound and ready for anything, this horse has never been shod.

Hooves of the
Rocky Mountain Stables

5 Year Old Percheron

Anyone who thinks draft horses have inferior hoof quality has never seen a fully transitioned barefoot marvel like this one tear up a gravel road!

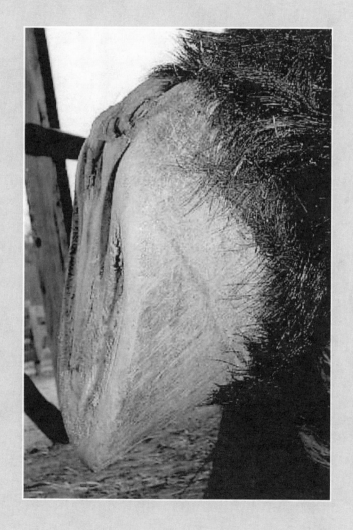

Making Natural Hoof Care Work for You

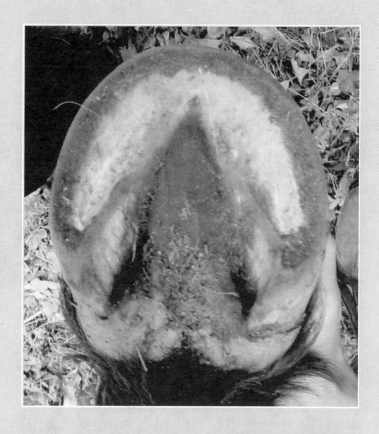

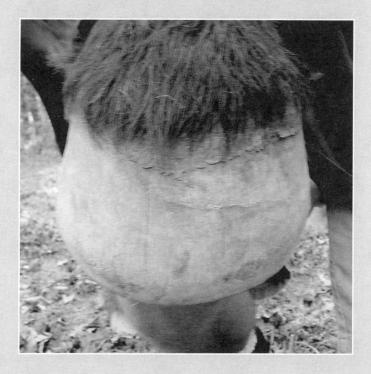

Hooves of the
Rocky Mountain Stables

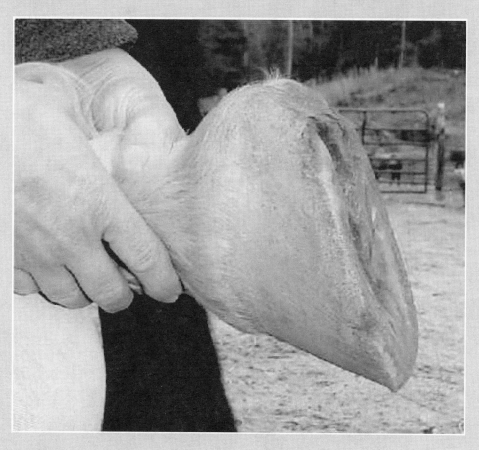

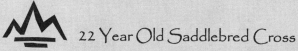 22 Year Old Saddlebred Cross

This used to be a navicular horse. He can sprint up the trail now, and is one of the most reliable horses on the mountain.

Making Natural Hoof Care Work for You

9 Year Old Percheron

This 2000 pound giant is a very agile, spirited ride that has been at the stables since he was two. He is used as a guide horse and is extremely capable anywhere with his thundering bare hooves.

Chapter 7
Transition

Transition

The most common question in a horse owner's mind is, "How long will it be before my horse is ready to ride?" If the natural trim is done correctly, there will be absolutely no pain *created* by it. Horses do usually need a few weeks for their hooves to callous enough for rough terrain. Other than that, there is actually no difference between transition and rehabilitation, and transition is actually a bad word to me. When a truly healthy hoof begins natural hoof care, there is no transitional time. They will perform better from the start. The only reason we have a transitional period at all is that most of the time we are starting out with problems that need to be healed. It is a fact that a healthy hoof can perform barefoot. If a hoof can't perform without protection we must figure out why and fix it. Assuming the trimming is correct, the transition time will depend on the following four primary factors:

Diet, exercise, the beginning condition of the hooves, and how well your horse will be expected to perform.

Diet

Lush pasture turnouts, and sweet high-carb type grain diets, most horses are on today are pure poison to their systems. Try to make your horse's diet as natural as possible. If your horse has foundered, this is more important than the trimming. If not, a healthy, natural diet can still give major advantages to your horse. I already explained how I personally feed horses, and half of mine are founder rehabs. A horse at work may need extra calories, but a vast majority of domestic horses on the very finest feeds and supplements would be much healthier with only free choice grass hay.

Exercise

Horses were born to move. Almost every serious hoof condition we need to rehabilitate involves growing a new hoof. Nature has provided the horse with a growth and adaptation system that is perfect for the abrasive lands it was born to roam. Because of increased blood flow through the hoof capsule, every time the hoof hits the ground, it grows a little to compensate for the wear, so hoof growth is more accurately measured in miles instead of time. This is why a working horse grows hoof so much quicker than a horse in close confinement. Anything you can do to encourage movement will speed up hoof growth and thus rehabilitation.

I am not in favor of force-walking lame horses but prefer to come up with tricks to encourage movement. I worked on a particularly bossy mare that was chronically foundered. The owner put her in a paddock with a gelding that the mare absolutely despised and three hay piles, twenty yards apart. The mare hobbled her way into total soundness trying to keep that agile gelding from eating. I learn every day.

Provide as much movement as possible while simply following your heart and using common sense. If you are rehabilitating a foundered horse, daily walks are helpful as soon as the horse is able. As soon as the horse can be ridden on soft footing, do so. As the horse gets more and more able, increase the riding and let the footing get tougher. Don't push it. Never ride a limping horse, but don't let worry immobilize you either. If the hooves are properly trimmed they will improve with every step.

Quality hoof boots will *greatly* speed up this process. They can be used for exercise and then removed for turnout. I don't advise leaving them on when you aren't exercising the horse.

Our Starting Point

The most obvious factor that affects transition time is the degree of damage we must overcome. If the hooves are healthy, the horse can be ridden immediately on easy footing and it can be only a matter of days before the sole will callous enough for rougher terrain. This is actually very common for highly skilled practitioners. The point we need to get across is that the hoof was created to work hard without protection and it is not healthy if it cannot. We must determine why the hoof is sore and how long it will take to heal the problem.

Predicting the speed of recovery of lame feet is the single greatest challenge of rehabilitation. Learning what to do is pretty easy, but telling the owner what to expect is a real challenge. If, for instance, a hoof is completely torn away from the coffin bone all the way around and the sole is flat or bulging, we know that the hoof won't be normal until we have grown an entire new healthy hoof capsule. I have seen such horses be unsound for the entire duration of this growth cycle. But I have also seen the same horses, once given the benefits of natural trimming, become comfortable on rough terrain immediately after the flaring hoof wall was removed and the white line tearing was stopped at the first trim, even though there was no support at all by the hoof wall. I know they will recover, but everyone wants to know when.

A long term nightmare of a founder case will usually "sound out" quicker than a horse that has recently foundered, but I think this is due to increased pain tolerance in the horse that has been lame for years. They seem to respond gleefully to the slightest relief. I generally tell people it will take longer than I actually think. I'd rather see them pleasantly surprised instead of finding myself making excuses. Learn all you can. The more hard cases you see, the better you will predict the duration of pain. If you ever develop the ability to predict it consistently, please find me and teach me how, because attempting to give time predictions continues to be the only thing I dislike about this business.

Expectations

The final factor I will discuss is owner expectations. If you are rehabilitating a lame pasture pet, your progress will be much more impressive than if you are rehabilitating a horse whose owner likes to ride on gravel roads. If you are dealing with the latter, provide quality hoof boots for riding. They can

shed the boots when the horse is ready, but they will get the owner on the horse quicker, and provide much-needed exercise.

Horses that are used barefoot on rough terrain need conditioning. Aside from all of the hoof health issues we have discussed, there is a "toughening up" factor as well. They need to get used to their new hoof form and being without shoes. I recommend that you work a horse in gradually to rough terrain, either by using hoof boots for some of the longer rides or by taking a few shorter rides to break them in gently. Again, let your heart be the guide and treat your horse the same way you would treat yourself if it was you who was being conditioned to go barefoot.

Aside from rocky roads and trails, horses will usually be ready to ride long before rehabilitation is complete. A shod performance horse with decent hooves will normally get faster, smoother, and more agile in the arena sand on day one, after his shoes are pulled. The self cleaning concavity of naturally shaped hooves digs in dirt like no shoe ever could. Since most competition is held on loose footing, horse owners generally see only dramatic improvement in performance from day one. It is the backwoods trail horse that actually poses the greatest challenge, but also the greatest advantages by being barefoot. Once trail riders experience the rugged surefootedness of a barefoot horse, the slippery nature of metal horseshoes on rock scares them to death and they are spoiled forever.

Patience

It is very important to remember where you started and where you are going. We set out to grow the hoof from the coronet to the ground in a straight line with no flares or dishing. If there are splits present, or destroyed white line, or some other problem, they must almost always be repaired by growing a new hoof. This can seem like a painfully slow process. You can know you are headed in the right direction if you train yourself to always judge hooves from the coronet down. Watching a steep, beautiful hoof grow down from the hairline is much more fun than staring for months at hoof cracks at ground level. It is also more accurate. If, on the other hand, cracks or flaring invade your new growth band, you will notice immediately and you must correct the mistake you are making.

Life Without Shoes

By far the most common compliment I hear about natural hoof care is that the horses are ready to ride when the horse owner is. People are sick of planning a big ride only to find that their horse has thrown a shoe. That was the original reason I learned to shoe myself. I also get piles of reports of increased performance in speed, agility, traction, attitude, smoothness, endurance, and the list goes on. The added shock absorption brings relief to almost every locomotion ailment you can think of from back pain to joint, muscle and tendon problems. I have seen many old horses whose owners thought were too arthritic to ride become a vision of vigor and health as soon as natural care was begun.

I guess the only complaint I hear is about the constant maintenance. Unfortunately, the vast majority of horse owners are used to neglecting their hooves for long periods of time. For the most part, I don't do business with such folks. People everywhere need to get it in their heads that routine hoof maintenance is part of owning a horse. You simply can't go for months at a time without hoof care and expect a long healthy life out of your horse. This is not "barefoot talk." It should be common knowledge (or common sense).

It is a fact that the horses at our trail riding stable improved when the shoes were removed. Remember, it hasn't been long since I was a skeptic myself, but it sounded right, so we tried it. When those horses were shod, they considered it normal for two or three of them to be sore after a busy weekend. They would treat their ailments and give them as much time off as they needed. They were working hard and that country is rough. The owners just considered it "part of the deal". Suddenly natural hoof care brought them horses that never seemed to get tired or sore. The added shock absorption of bare hooves more than makes up for the weight of the rider, and horses sim-

Making Natural Hoof Care Work for You

ply perform better and longer. Sure, the owners liked the "idea" of having barefoot horses, but they were running a business that demands the horses be in top condition. If natural hoof care hadn't improved the capability of the horses, they definitely would have forgotten the whole thing really quick and had me nail on some shoes. Sure, I am a 100% barefoot advocate now, because I have seen it with my own eyes, but back then I was a horseshoer just trying an experiment. The dramatic improvement was a big deal for us all, and I've seen it repeated for others countless times since.

I am promoting an idea here more than a method. If we can get vets, farriers, and horse owners to pay attention and start studying natural horses, I can only assume this book will become obsolete as more is learned. Believe it or not, that will be the best news ever.

Hoof Boots

Hoof boots are a valuable tool for any natural hoof care program. For years farriers have experimented to find a better horseshoe, and the boot is the future "shoe". At this writing, the only hoof boots I have seen or heard of that really work well must be heat fitted and modified by a professional on site. This is a disadvantage since boot specialists are few and far between at this time. (We're working on that.) If you can find a boot specialist in your area, the boots work great, once you get them fitted. They are easy to deal with, and I have seen them get well over 500 miles of serious trail riding without trouble. As demand increases, more heads will be put to the problem, and companies will come up with better and better boots.

For now, the biggest advantage I see is that they get owners of horses in rehabilitation on their horses sooner. Usually, as soon as a foundered horse gets comfortable on soft footing barefoot, it can be comfortably ridden almost anywhere in hoof boots. They can also be necessary if the terrain you ride on is drastically different from where the horse lives.

Hoof boots also give peace of mind to horse owners who are convinced their horses need protection, and they can always be used as an insurance pol-

icy on a long trail ride in the middle of nowhere. They are very convenient because they are ready to go whenever you are and they offer far better and more complete protection than nailed on shoes.

Obviously, I always work toward our wild model and I have found that the closer a hoof gets to it, the fewer problems it will have, but a boot can be a big help along the way. I highly recommend that anyone who is going to trim for a living go through the "Certified Practitioner" training program of the American Association of Natural Hoof Care Practitioners (On the Internet, check out the AANHCP at: www.aanhcp.org).

Making Natural Hoof Care Work for You